This is what he looked like at the very beginning!

1978 1978 1978 1978 1978 1978 1978 1978 1978 1978

Dear Reader

It's hard to believe 21 years have passed since Garfield first made his debut in the funny papers. Back then he was grouchy, lazy, fat, rude and self-indulgent – turns out he was just getting warmed up.

To celebrate the curmudgeonly kitty's coming of age, we've compiled a mile of strips and dozens of stories and tossed in some interesting little titbits on the side to bring you Garfield's 21st Birthday Celebration Book.

This book celebrates the life and times of the lasagne-loving, coffee-guzzling, nap-taking, spider-whacking, dog-punting, postman-eating fat cat in all his orange-furred glory.

It's been a long, strange journey from Garfield's humble beginnings as a lowly comic strip character, to his rise to the top as the world's favourite cat. So, join Garfield and me as we skip down memory lane. Actually, sometimes we have to DRAG Garfield dowm memory lane; nonetheless, it's quite a journey, which I think you'll enjoy.

Thanks for your many years of kind devotion. Your efforts have helped make Garfield's 21st Birthday Celebration Book possible.

Best Wishes

Jim Davis

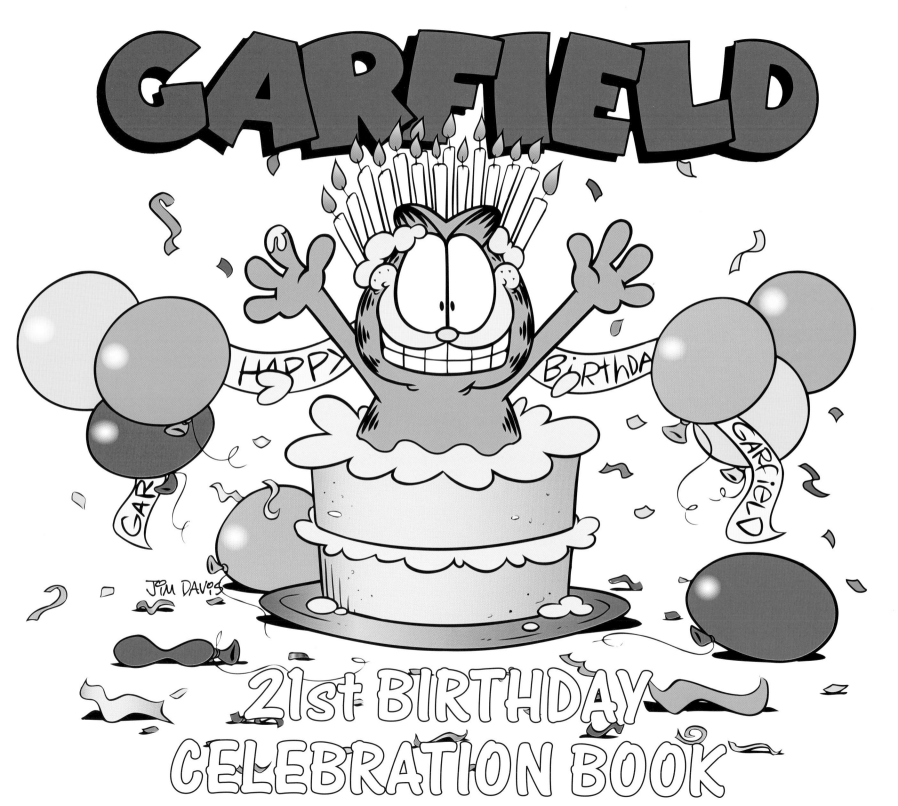

CONTENTS

Written and edited by Gordon Volke.
Design and layouts by GRAPHIC Group. Repro and setting by Formaprint Ltd.
Printed and bound by Proost N.V. Belgium.

This first edition published in 1999 by Ravette Publishing Limited,
Unit 3, Tristar Centre, Star Road, Partridge Green, West Sussex RH13 8RA

ISBN: 1-84161-002-X

The week commencing June 19th, 1978, was a momentous one. A young cricketer called Ian Botham burst onto the Test scene, scoring a century for England and then taking 8 Pakistan wickets for only 34 runs – almost winning the Test Match on his own. In Argentina, the host nation won the World Cup Final, beating Holland in a thrilling match that went into extra time.

And, in America, a superstar was born.

Garfield made his debut in 41 American newspapers on the Monday of this week. In these early strips, Garfield does not look quite the same as he does today.

Here are the main differences:

* His body was larger.

* His eyes were much smaller.

* His mouth was also much smaller.

* His ears were more pointed.

* His nose was T-shaped instead of oval.

* He had lots of dots on his top lip and cheeks.

* He had many more stripes.

* He had more than three whiskers either side of his face.

Jon also looked different, though not as much as Garfield. His face was thinner, his eyes were much smaller and his hair was a bit longer (well, it was the Seventies!) Also, Jon introduced himself as a cartoonist, but this occupation was eventually phased out of the strip. Nowadays, Jon finds it a full-time job just to look after Garfield.

What hasn't changed, of course, is the essential characters of Garfield and Jon. Right from the beginning, Garfield was a fat, greedy, lazy and demanding cat, and Jon was a muddle-headed, good-natured nerd! Judge for yourself as we travel back in time to the happiest week of the Seventies and revisit the first six GARFIELD® daily strips and first Sunday strip...

I like being a cat of the nineties — ninety stone, ninety meals a day, ninety hours sleep a week…!

7

THE MAIN MAN

Biography Of
Jim Davis

In The Beginning...

Jim Davis was born in Marion, Indiana, USA on July 28th, 1945. He grew up on a small farm near Fairmont, Indiana, with his mother, father and brother, Dave (nicknamed "Doc"). The farm boasted a herd of cattle and an assortment of 25 cats, so the young Jim Davis received an early education in feline behaviour.

Degree Of Success

Jim Davis left High School in 1963 and moved on to Ball State University in Muncie, Indiana. He studied Art and Business but was more interested in the social life of the college than in his chosen subjects. As a result: "I distinguished myself by earning one of the lowest cumulative grade point averages in the history of the university!"

Even so, this lack of academic success did not prevent the 22-year old Davis from getting a job.

Those Who Can Read – Should!

During his childhood years, Jim Davis suffered very badly from asthma. He had to stay indoors a lot and, to pass the time, his mother encouraged him to draw. She was a talented artist herself and taught the young cartoonist many useful techniques. As well as drawing and writing, Jim spent his time reading – especially newspaper comic strips. He learned a great deal from studying classic cartoons such as 'Peanuts' and 'Prince Valiant'.

Learning The Trade

For the first two years after leaving University, Jim worked for an advertising agency. His job was to design layouts for catalogues and brochures. Then, in 1969, he moved on to become assistant to Tom Ryan, an established cartoonist whose 'Tumbleweeds' strip was already being printed in the newspapers. Working for Ryan, Jim Davis learned the ins and outs of producing a daily cartoon strip.

Gnat Trainer

During his time with Tom Ryan, Jim Davis devoted his spare time to developing his own comic strip. It was called 'Gnorm Gnat' and featured a weird assortment of insect characters including Dr. Rosenwurm, who recited poetry, and Cecil Slug, who was very stupid. The strip appeared in one Indiana newspaper for some years, but the frustrated young cartoonist failed to interest anyone else. As one editor put it:

"Your art is good, your gags are great, but bugs – nobody can identify with bugs!"

But Jim was not beaten – not by a long shot. He had a new idea up his sleeve...

Enter The Fat Cat

Jim Davis realised that a number of existing strips featured dogs (Snoopy, Marmaduke, Fred Basset), but few featured cats. So he invented a large, bad-tempered orange cat and named him Garfield after his grandfather, James A. Garfield

Davis. Then it took another eighteen months to perfect the characters and polish the humour which, right from the start, was kept broad and straightforward so as to appeal to the widest possible audience. At last the material was ready and Jim Davis sent a package of sample strips to various American newspaper syndicates.

Let's Hear It For United Media

At first, the results were not encouraging. King Features (who publishes Popeye) turned him down. And United Media was not interested because it was already considering another cat character from an established cartoonist. Then, for some unknown reason (Jim believes it was fate!), United Media decided to drop this rival cat and expressed an interest in GARFIELD®. More sample strips had to be submitted and, in January 1978, at the height of the worst snowstorm Indiana had known for years, Jim Davis received the golden phone call. United Media had accepted GARFIELD®.

Out To Launch

There seems to be an unwritten rule in publishing that everything has to be done in a terrible hurry! This was certainly the case with Garfield's launch. Jim thought he had six months to get ready, but United Media brought the release date forward and he found he only had two weeks! So he burned the midnight oil and managed to produce all the material they wanted within the deadline. Then, as we all know, Garfield made his first appearance in 41 American newspapers on June 19th, 1978.

Early Days

Garfield was an immediate success. The policy of keeping the humour broad paid off handsomely and people found themselves relating to this cynical, food-loving and exercise-hating cat. (He was just like them!) In fact, when a Chicago newspaper talked about dropping Garfield after three months, a legion of over 1,300 irate fans wrote in to protest. The fab feline had a loyal following right from the start.

Expanding The Cast

Jim Davis was now free to expand and develop his established strip.

Jon, of course, had been right there from the start. (His name, by the way, was taken from an old coffee advert that Jim remembered from the past.) Odie made his first appearance on August 10th, 1978. His name, too, came from a commercial – only, this time, Jim had written it himself! It was a radio advert that Jim had penned in the early Seventies for a local car dealer. It featured Odie, the village idiot, and the name seemed perfect for his new idiot dog!

Pooky came next. Garfield found his special teddy in a drawer on October 23rd, 1978, and they have been inseparable ever since. The same can't be said of Nermal whose cute kitten features were first seen on September 3rd, 1978. (Originally, he belonged to Jon's parents, but this idea gave way to Nermal being a neighbourhood friend who appears from time to time.) Arlene was the last major player to arrive. She made her debut as Garfield's gap-toothed and long-suffering girlfriend on December 17th, 1980.

Finally, there's just room to mention Lyman. Poor old Lyman! He appeared in a lot of the early strips as Jon's roommate and Odie's owner. But he was axed in 1983 and has never really been seen since. Sad, isn't it?

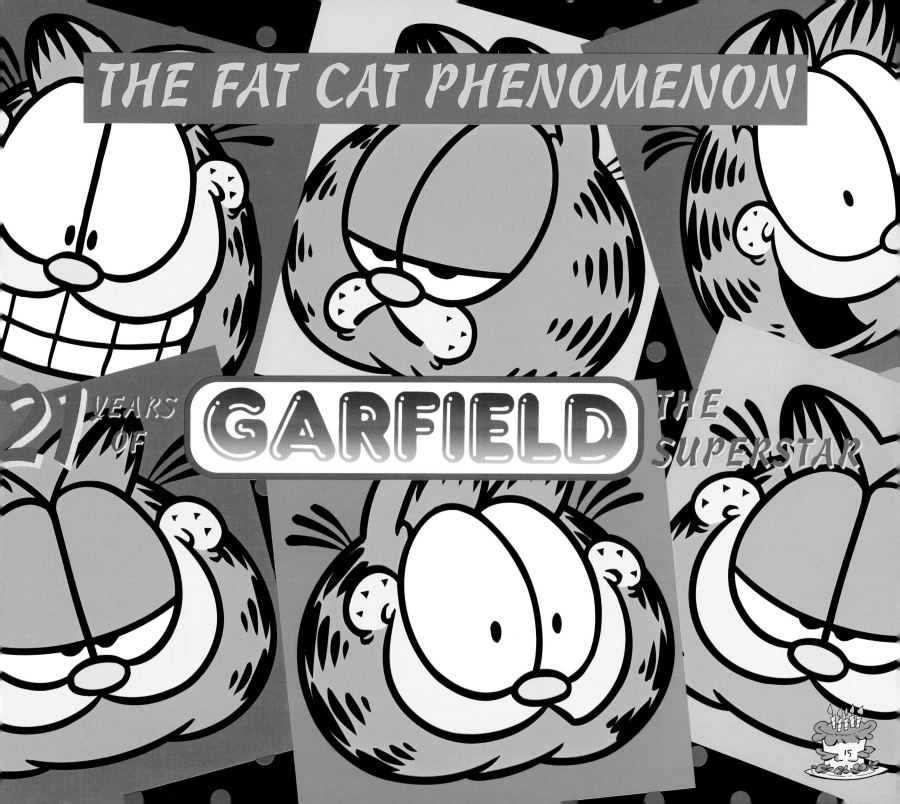

THE FAT CAT PHENOMENON

21 YEARS OF GARFIELD THE SUPERSTAR

15

Garfield The Book Baron

By 1980, a mere two years after his launch, Garfield was appearing in over 100 newspapers. The fat cat was proving himself a big hit with the public and Jim Davis felt that it was time to branch out. He wanted to have collections of his new strip reprinted in book form.

To allow Garfield to be printed horizontally, as he is in the newspapers, the cartoonist invented a new shaped book. It was wide and "sideways on" (just like this birthday book). At first, the book trade was a bit dubious, but soon changed it's mind when the books started selling well. Today, the format is well established and any sideways shaped book is called a "Garfield format" book.

This type of Garfield book was, of course, just the beginning. Since the early Eighties, hundreds of millions of Garfield books have been sold on both sides of the Atlantic and around the world. And they've come in all shapes and sizes, paperback and hardback – even a miniature storybook with cardboard pages that you can hang on your Christmas tree!

Garfield The Media Mogul

Obviously, exposure in an ever-

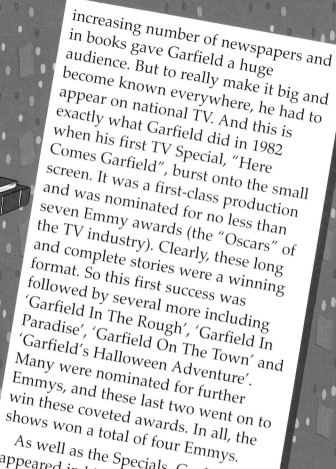

increasing number of newspapers and in books gave Garfield a huge audience. But to really make it big and become known everywhere, he had to appear on national TV. And this is exactly what Garfield did in 1982 when his first TV Special, "Here Comes Garfield", burst onto the small screen. It was a first-class production and was nominated for no less than seven Emmy awards (the "Oscars" of the TV industry). Clearly, these long and complete stories were a winning format. So this first success was followed by several more including 'Garfield In The Rough', 'Garfield In Paradise', 'Garfield On The Town' and 'Garfield's Halloween Adventure'. Many were nominated for further Emmys, and these last two went on to win these coveted awards. In all, the shows won a total of four Emmys.

As well as the Specials, Garfield also appeared in his own TV series, 'Garfield And Friends'. Here, he was seen in much shorter stories and shared the stage with Jim Davis' other creation, 'Orson's Farm'. 'Garfield And Friends' proved to be as popular as the longer programmes and was shown worldwide, including a long run on ITV and Sky in the UK where they are still being shown.

Garfield The International Magazine Megastar

As Garfield's tenth birthday approached, the company that published Garfield books in Germany came up with a bright idea. "Let's bring out a special tenth birthday magazine!" they suggested.

To reduce the cost of this project, they asked the other Garfield book publishers in Europe if they would like to join in and produce co-editions. The idea was that the same strips and editorial features would be used in every edition, but the language would be changed. The idea was a rip-roaring success! In the UK, the magazine sold like the proverbial hot cakes and had to be reprinted several times before demand was satisfied. This led to another idea – if this is such a success, why not do it every month? And so the pan-European Garfield monthly magazine was born!

The first magazine in this long-running series appeared at the end of 1989. As well as Germany and Britain, the other partners were France, Spain, Norway, Sweden, Finland and Denmark. As time went on, some countries dropped out and others joined in, including Hungary and Greece. In the UK, the magazine notched up huge sales in its early years and ran, with a wide-ranging and loyal readership, until 1995. In the Scandinavian countries, Greece, Hungary, Poland and Turkey, it is still going strong to this day.

The Garfield Magazine featured Garfield strips, both new and classic; 'Orson's Farm' strips; a colourful, pull-out poster; special features; a letters page and a penpals page. The latter was extremely popular and the waiting list to have your name published ran to several months. Many youngsters from different countries all around the world have got to know each other, thanks to Garfield.

Highlights of Garfield's First 10 Years

June 19 1978	GARFIELD® Introduced in 41 newspapers.
March 1980	The first GARFIELD book, 'Garfield At Large' hits No 1 on The New York Times Best Sellers List.
April 1981	GARFIELD appears in 500 newspapers.
May 1981	GARFIELD appears in 1,000 newspapers. Davis wins the 'Best Humour Strip' award from the National Cartoonists Society.
November '82	Seven GARFIELD books appear on The New York Times Best Sellers List, a world record.
1982	'Here Comes Garfield' animated television special is nominated for two Emmy awards.
September '84	'Garfield On The Town', the second animated television special, wins the Emmy Award for outstanding Animated Programme.
February 1985	21st Century Comics Research Group finds GARFIELD most popular comic strips. GARFIELD now appears in more than 1,500 newspapers in 22 countries and 7 languages.
September '85	Jim Davis wins his second Emmy Award for 'Garfield In The Rough'
November '85	Jim Davis wins the Segar Award from the National Cartoonists Society.
April 1986	Cartoon 'Q' study rates GARFIELD as the No.1 comic strip.
April 1986	Jim Davis wins 'Best Humour Strip' Award from the National Cartoonists Society.
August 1986	'Garfield's Halloween Adventure', and 'Garfield In Paradise' are nominated for Emmy Awards, the Halloween Special wins.
August 1987	GARFIELD becomes the third comic strip in history to appear in more than 2,000 newspapers.
June 1988	GARFIELD is ten years old.

Garfield the Licensing Lion!

Licensing is not a new idea. Beatrix Potter, at the beginning of this century, is known to have sewn the first doll of Peter Rabbit with her own fair hands. But it was not until the consumer-based Seventies and Eighties that the idea really took off. And Garfield was in the forefront of the movement.

Garfield soft toys were the first spin-off product of the newspaper/book/TV and magazine superstar. Known as "plush" toys, they varied in size and price from a huge, almost child-sized Garfield down to little ones that clipped on to your lapel. Perhaps the most famous of all was the "Stuck-On-You Garfield". This middle-sized toy was designed to stick onto car windows and, during the late Eighties, barely a car went past without Garfield's face grinning at you. Garfield soft toys are still being sold today by a company in Yorkshire.

As well as these dolls, almost everything else you can think of has, at one time or another, been produced in Garfield's shape or featuring Garfield's image. Duvet covers, greeting cards, pencil boxes and other stationery, money boxes, socks...the list is endless. Always, however, Garfield looked right on these products. Jim Davis and his company, PAWS, enforced strict rules to make sure that Garfield's image was the correct size, shape and colour. The policy has paid off. Any Garfield licenced product has always been a quality product.

WELL HE'S A FAT CAT, A COOL CAT,
NOBODY'S FOOL CAT, SO LOOK OUT
'CAUSE HERE COMES GARFIELD!
HE NEVER KEEPS FIT, HE'S TOO HIP,
HE LIKES HIS CATNIP, SO LOOK OUT
'CAUSE HERE COMES GARFIELD!

HE'S ALWAYS GOT TO BE "ONE UP" ON YA,
AND HE'LL BEAT YOU TO THE PUNCH
EVERYTIME,
HE'LL GIVE UP ANYTHING FOR LASAGNE,
UNLESS HE HAS TO GIVE UP HIS NAP-TIME!

BUT HE'S A NEAT CAT, A FUN CAT,
MISTER NUMBER ONE CAT,
HE KNOWS WHAT LIFE IS ALL ABOUT...
HERE COMES GARFIELD, LOOK OUT!
HERE COMES GARFIELD, LOOK OUT!
I SAID HERE COMES GARFIELD

The latest Garfield soft toy range

MUSIC TO OUR EARS!
The Voice Of Garfield

Actor, singer, writer, producer and all-round funnyman, LORENZO MUSIC is the voice of Garfield.

GARFIELD GOES TO HOLLYWOOD The fab feline stars in his sixth TV spectacular!

Garfield IN THE ROUGH The third spectacular TV SPECIAL starring the world's favourite cat JIM DAVIS

Garfield on the town The world's greatest cat in his second spectacular TV SPECIAL! By Jim Davis and Lorenzo Music

Garfield IN DISGUISE The world's favourite cat in his fourth spectacular TV SPECIAL! JIM DAVIS

19

One day during the late 1970s, Jim Davis was at home working on his new comic strip, GARFIELD. The cartoonist liked to have the television on while he worked and one of the shows he liked to watch was a sit-com called 'Rhoda'. Rhoda, a girl from Minneapolis now living in New York, had a doorman named Carlton. You never saw Carlton, you only ever heard his voice saying: "Hello, this is Carlton your doorman."

As soon as Jim Davis heard Carlton's voice, he knew it was exactly right for Garfield. The part of Carlton was played by Lorenzo Music.

When Jim Davis came to produce his first Garfield TV Special, 'Here Comes Garfield', he invited Lorenzo Music to audition for the part of the fat cat. The job has been his ever since. Anyone who has watched the series of award-winning TV Specials that followed, or the popular TV series 'Garfield and Friends', will have heard "the sound of Music"...Lorenzo Music, that is!

This instant success was no flash-in-the-pan. Behind it lies a long and distinguished career in American show business. Lorenzo Music was born in New York and brought up in Minnesota. At Minnesota University, he met his wife and they formed a comedy duo, performing at clubs and colleges during the 'folk boom' of the early 1960s. The arrival of the first of their four children put and end to 'Jerry and Myrna Music', as their act was called, and Lorenzo Music turned his attention to writing.

It was a natural progression for the humorous and talented young man. In 1968, after only one year on the writing staff of the TV show, 'The Smothers Brothers Comedy Hour', Lorenzo Music won an Emmy (the television equivalent of an Oscar) for 'outstanding achievement in comedy writing'. During the 1970s he went on to write, edit, and produce a long series of classic TV comedy shows, many of which have been shown in this country. The list includes 'The Mary Tyler Moore Show', 'The Bob Newhart Show' and the aforementioned 'Rhoda'.

Then came Garfield...and the rest, as they say, is history.

Nowadays, Lorenzo Music lives in Los Angeles where he continues to work in the field of comedy. It is his distinctive voice, however, that is most in demand. As well as Garfield, he is the voice of Tummy Gummi in 'The Gummi Bears' and Peter Venkman in 'The Real Ghostbusters'. In addition to all this cartoon work, he has recorded countless radio and TV commercials, making him one of the best-known voices in the field of American advertising.

No doubt by now you are wondering what this multi-talented showbiz personality looks like. Until recently you would have remained in the dark because Lorenzo Music was always reluctant to show his face in public. Why? Because he felt that to let people see what he looked like would destroy the illusion created by his voice. He once explained: "If people saw a picture of me, they would say, "He looks like that instead of Garfield!" If you have a visual image, it takes away from what you hear."

21

WHAT'S IN A NAME?

(A lasagne by any other name would taste as sweet!)

As you may know, Jim Davis took the name 'Garfield' from his grandfather, James A. Garfield Davis. So we decided to find out where Mr. Davis Senior got the name from, and also what the name means.

Taking the second question first, a dictionary of American names states that 'GARFIELD' means: "DWELLER ON THE GRASSY LAND OR PASTURE".

It appears that the name is of English origin, but we could not find a similar entry in a dictionary of English family names. So it would seem that its early use was exclusively American.

The name 'Garfield' became famous with the election of James Garfield as 20th President of the United States in November, 1880. President Garfield had only been in office for about four months when he was attacked and badly wounded by a rival at the railway station in Washington D.C. The unfortunate President never properly recovered from the attack and was succeeded by his Vice President, Chester A. Arthur, in November 1881.

To honour President Garfield, several places in America changed their name – Garfield Heights in Cleveland, Ohio, being one example. And many people, including Jim Davis' early family, adopted 'Garfield' as an extra middle name.

So now you know!

HEY, BUDDY, MAKE THAT: 'DWELLER ON THE COMFY BED OR SOFA!

22

Jon Arbuckle

Jon has recently established itself as an independent name, but originally it was a shortened form of *Jonathan*. It means "gift of the Lord". Both *Jon* and *Jonathan* have been widely used in America, the British preferring to stick with the more traditional *John*.

Arbuckle is a Scottish name originating from Airdrie in the old county of Lanarkshire. It comes from the Gaelic "ard an buachaille" which means "height of the shepherd". The first recorded use of the name was in 1499.

Given that Jon has doting parents who live on a farm in the country, his name is very appropriate – especially as Garfield dwells on the grassy land or pasture!

Hubert And Reba

Hubert is an old German name meaning "a bright or shining mind". It is rare as a first name these days, but is connected with a number of surnames including Hubbard (as in Old Mother Hubbard of nursery rhyme fame).

During the 8th century, there was a *Saint Hubert* who was the patron saint of hunters. Perhaps that's why Hubert is always chasing Garfield out of his garden!

Reba is a shortened form of *Rebecca*, a very famous Hebrew name meaning "the captivator". A survey during the 1980s showed that *Rebecca* in its various forms was the fifth most popular name in the United Kingdom.

Liz

Jon's would-be girlfriend, Liz the vet, has one of the best known names in the country – Elizabeth. Since the reign of Queen Elizabeth 1st (1558-1603), the name has been the third most popular in Britain. (The other two are *Mary* and *Ann*.) As well as *Liz*, *Elizabeth* has many other shortened forms including *Bess, Bessie, Beth, Betty, Eliza, Lisa, Elsie, Elsbeth and Libby* (to name but a few!). The name is of Hebrew origin and means "given to God".

© PAWS

23

Arlene

Arlene is a variation of *Aline,* a name that did not come into use until the beginning of this century. There are two schools of thought about what it means. Some say *Arline* is a Gaelic word meaning "pledge". Others think the name is a corruption of *Charlene,* a German word meaning "strong and womanly". In either case, the descriptions fit Arlene very well – she is loyal to Garfield (despite his chauvinist indifference to her), and she is a girl who definitely knows her own mind!

Irma

Irma, the waitress at the restaurant often visited by Jon and Garfield, has a German name that means "the healer". *Irma* is actually a variant of *Emma,* another popular English forename. The name fits well with Irma's character because, despite working so hard that she is almost asleep on her feet, she will always lend a sympathetic ear to her customers' troubles.

© PAWS

Jim Davis

Jim is a shortened form of *James*. The name is of Hebrew origin and means " the supplanter". Along with its feminine form, *Jacqueline, James* is one of the most widely used names in the Western world.

Davis is a variant of *David*, another Hebrew name meaning "beloved". The name has been popular since Biblical times, King David being one of the greatest Kings of ancient Israel.

Put together, Jim Davis' name means:

"The beloved supplanter."

What could be more apt? Jim Davis has supplanted all other cartoonists by creating Garfield, the world's most popular and widely read newspaper cartoon character.

THE CREAM OF GARFIELD

Top Twenty Daily Strips – Updated

About ten years ago, we asked Jim Davis to pick his twenty favourite Garfield daily strips. He duly obliged and the selection was published in the 1991 Garfield Annual under the title of 'Garfield's Top Twenty'.

Obviously, since then a great deal of newsprint has flowed under the bridge and this original selection is now out of date. So, for the purposes of this celebration book, we've asked Garfield's creator to think again and we're pleased to report that he's updated his previous selection to include the two and a half thousand or so daily strips he has drawn since the start of the decade.

Here's the result – twenty classic Garfield strips chosen for being among Jim Davis' favourites. This is the Cream Of Garfield...

ARE WE HAVING FUN YET?

DID I HEAR SOMEONE SAY 'CREAM'?

JUNE 9TH, 1979

DECEMBER 25TH, 1981

JULY 13TH, 1982

APRIL 25TH, 1983

OCTOBER 18TH, 1983

JANUARY 3RD, 1984

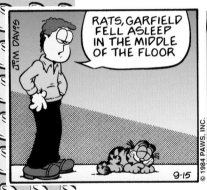

SEPTEMBER 15TH, 1984

APRIL 4TH, 1987

28

AUGUST 20TH, 1988

MAY 30TH, 1989

JUNE 10TH, 1989

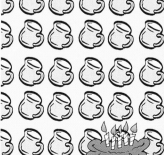

29

NOVEMBER 6TH, 1989

FEBRUARY 8TH, 1990

MARCH 8TH, 1991

JUNE 20TH, 1991

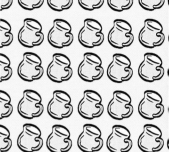

MAY 7TH, 1992

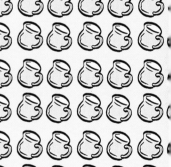

APRIL 2ND, 1993

"I'VE COME OVER ALL GOOSE-PIMPLES. DON'T KNOW IF IT'S THOSE STRIPS, OR THE FACT THAT ODIE'S JUST SHUT MY TAIL IN THE DOOR!"

SNIFF

(JON)
"DO YOU LIKE KIPLING, GARFIELD?"

(GARFIELD)
"WOULDN'T KNOW – I'VE NEVER KIPPLED!"

A Poem

(With apologies to Mr Kipling who makes **exceedingly** good poetry)

On the occasion of his 21st birthday, Garfield has taken it upon himself to give some fatherly advice to Nermal the kitten...

IF YOU CAN SLEEP ALL DAY WHEN ALL AROUND YOU
IS BUSTLE, MESS AND NOISE,
AND THEN FEEL TIRED AND SLEEP ALL NIGHT
WITH JUST A SINGLE CUDDLY TOY;

IF YOU CAN EAT LASAGNE, PIZZA
AND ALL FORMS OF PASTA
UNTIL THEY'RE COMING OUT OF YOUR EARS,
AND WATCH A DOG CHASE A DINGLE BALL
WITHOUT BEING COMPLETELY REDUCED TO TEARS;

IF YOU CAN KICK THAT DOG LIKE A RUGBY PLAYER
WEARING BOOTS AND ALL THE CLOBBER,
AND SIT ON THE SOFA NEXT TO THE DOG
WITHOUT DROWNING IN HIS SLOBBER;

IF YOU CAN CLIMB A TREE TO THE HIGHEST BRANCH
WITHOUT ONCE EVER GETTING STUCK,
AND WATCH TWO GLANDULAR HUMANS KISS
WITHOUT JUMPING UP AND SHOUTING "YUK";

IF YOU CAN ATTACK THE POSTMAN EVERY DAY
IN AN ORIGINAL AND CREATIVE WAY,
AND MAKE ALL THE DECISIONS IN YOUR HOUSE
WITHOUT YOUR MASTER HAVING A SAY;

IF YOU SQUISH A FAT AND HAIRY SPIDER
WITH A SWIFT AND EVEN HAIRIER THUMB,
THEN BREAK A WINDOW OR EXPENSIVE VASE
AND BLAME SOMEONE ELSE, OR JUST KEEP MUM;

IF YOU CAN SURF A HUNDRED TV CHANNELS
UNTIL YOUR REMOTE IS SMOKING HOT,
AND WATCH BINKY THE CLOWN WHILST FALLING ASLEEP
WITHOUT FOR A MOMENT LOSING THE PLOT;

IF YOU CAN LOVE YOURSELF MORE THAN ANYONE ELSE,
(ESPECIALLY MORE THAN YOUR GIRL),
AND PLAY SAD GAMES ON A SATURDAY NIGHT –
GAMES THAT MAKE YOUR TOES CURL;

IF YOU CAN SHRED A CHAIR IN SECONDS,
AND LEAVE THE CURTAINS HANGING IN SHREDS,
IF YOU CAN EAT YOUR BREAKFAST, LUNCH AND TEA
(PLUS SNACKS)
WITHOUT EVER GETTING OUT OF BED;

IF YOU START YOUR CHRISTMAS LIST IN JUNE
BECAUSE YOU'VE GOT SO MUCH TO WRITE,
AND YOU BREAK YOUR NEW YEAR'S RESOLUTION
AT EXACTLY ONE MINUTE PAST MIDNIGHT;

IF YOU NEED TEN CUPS OF COFFEE
JUST TO KICK-START YOUR BRAIN,
AND YOU SAY OF THOSE WHO EXERCISE –
"THEY HAVE A THING FOR PAIN";

IF YOU CAN DANCE ON THE GARDEN FENCE
AND ENTERTAIN THE CROWD,
IF YOU EAT BIRDS AND FROGS AND GOLDFISH TOO,
EVEN THOUGH IT'S NOT ALLOWED;

IF YOU'RE GREEDY, FAT AND LAZY,
SELFISH TO THE CORE,
A SUPERSTAR WHO GETS ALL THE LAUGHS
AND LEAVES 'EM WANTING MORE...

THEN YOU'LL BE A CAT, MY SON!

WITH VERY BEST SQUISHES

Revenge Of The Spiders

"If you want to live and thrive," says the old proverb, "let a spider run alive."

"NAH!" says Garfield. "Squish 'em!"

So far, in his war against the arachnids, Garfield has had it all his own way. The spiders in his house have been subjected to a bombardment of rolled-up newspapers, swatters and big orange thumbs! But for how long will this continue?

Using their World Wide Web, the spiders have called for reinforcements – their big brothers from overseas. These guys (if you'll excuse the mixed metaphor) are a completely different kettle of fish. How will Garfield fare against them? How would YOU fare against them?

Turn over to find out...

WHEN I SQUISH 'EM THEY STAY SQUISHED!

HEY! I THOUGHT I SQUISHED YOU YESTERDAY!

NAH

YOU ONLY GOT MY LEG

WANNA SIGN MY CAST?

JIM DAVIS 6-4

© 1997 PAWS, INC./Distributed by Universal Press Syndicate

36

THE TRAP-DOOR SPIDER

This type of spider gets its name from its unique method of catching its food. Trap-door spiders dig a hole in the ground and then build a door at the top, hinged with silk. The spider hides inside the hole and, when it hears the vibrations of an approaching insect, it flips up the door, grabs its startled prey and drags it down into the hole.

These spiders, which are found in places as far apart as Japan and Africa, live deep down in their holes except when hunting food. Some holes have tunnels leading off the main tube and these may also have doors to the outside world.

THE BIRD-EATING SPIDER

The Bird-Eating Spider is remarkable because of the size of the prey it is able to catch. As its name implies, this spider mainly eats small birds, but it has also been known to catch lizards, frogs and snakes. (To date there is no record of one catching a cat, so Garfield can relax in this case! Bird-Eating Spiders have a pair of downward-pointing fangs which they sink into their victim and then inject with poison.

These tropical spiders also have an interesting form of defence. When attacked by a large bird or a hunting wasp, the Bird-Eating Spider kicks off the hairs from its back legs which irritate the eyes and nose of its enemy, making him retreat.

37

THE BLACK WIDOW SPIDER

'Black Widow' is the popular American name for a group of spiders also found in Africa, the Middle East, Australia and New Zealand. Unlike the tarantula, they are not very big, but they are greatly feared because of their poisonous bite. If you are unlucky enough to be attacked by a Black Widow, you will experience great pain, sickness and difficulty in breathing. Fortunately, though, the bite is rarely fatal and most victims recover to tell the tale.

You seldom see a male Black Widow spider. The male is only a quarter the size of the female and is often killed and eaten by her after mating!

THE TARANTULA

The tarantula is a huge, hairy spider found in southern Europe, the United States, Mexico and South America. Its body can grow up to 2cm wide and its leg span is in the region of 12cm. (That's about the size of a grown man's fist!) At one time tarantulas were thought to be poisonous, but this has now been shown not to be the case. They can inflict a very painful bite if annoyed. They also live for a very long time, some for about 30 years.

Tarantulas are unusual spiders in that they do not spin a web to catch their food. Instead, they pursue their prey along the ground. They feed mainly at night, eating insects, small frogs and toads, and mice.

GARFIELD'S TOP TEN TENS

Garfield isn't just funny in picture strip form or on TV, he's funny in print, too. And one of the favourite formats of the Garfield writers is the "Top Ten". Here, Garfield lists his attitudes and opinions on various subjects in order of importance from 10 to 1. It's proved to be a rich vein of humour in the past and here are some classic examples, both new and old...

GARFIELD'S TOP TEN FAMOUS QUOTATIONS

10. Henry Ford:
"People can have it in any colour – so long as it's orange and black."

9. Samuel Johnson:
"When a man is tired of lasagne, he is tired of life."

8. Sherlock Holmes:
"Alimentary, my dear Watson."

7. Neville Chamberlain:
"I believe it is pizza for our time."

6. John Keats:
"A thing of beauty is a joy for eating."

5. John Donne:
"Never send to know for whom the bell tolls, it tolls for tea."

4. Aristotle:
"One swallow does not make a supper."

3. Descartes:
"I eat, therefore I am."

2. William Shakespeare:
"Some are born geeks, some achieve geekness, and some have geekness thrust upon them."

1. Garfield the Cat:
"Feed me."

GARFIELD'S TOP TEN REASONS FOR AVOIDING THE COUNTRYSIDE

10. The horrible smell of fresh air.

9. It's not natural.

8. Bigfoot might steal his picnic.

7. Trees are for dogs.

6. The steak is still walking about.

5. The birds are too big to swallow whole.

4. There's a strong possibility of meeting a vet.

3. "Show me a field full of cowpats and I'll show you a minefield in the dark."

2. The Waltons were always corny.

1. If you wait long enough, it becomes the town anyway.

TOP TEN OTHER POSSIBLE MEANINGS FOR THE NAME "ARBUCKLE"

10. "pigeon-chested"
9. "rash giver"
8. "pudding-brained"
7. "man of socks"
6. "dances with cows"
5. "he who giggles in battle"
4. "Uh-oh, here he comes"
3. "royal bore"
2. "village dweeb"
1. "cat-pecked"

ODIE'S TOP TEN CONFUSED CLICHÉS

10. In one nostril and out the other
9. Caught with his head in the cookie jar
8. All dressed up and no place to drool
7. Cold hands, warm liver
6. I'll be a donkey's uncle
5. His breath is worse than his bite
4. Between a rock and a hard-boiled egg
3. A new leash on life
2. Keep a stiff rubber lip
1. Two tongues are better than one

GARFIELD'S TOP TEN HIT RECORDS OF ALL TIME

10. **Neil Sedaka:**
    WAKING UP IS HARD TO DO

9. **The Beatles:**
    FREE AS A NERD

8. **The Bee Gees:**
    HOW DEEP IS YOUR LASAGNE?

7. **Peter Shelley:**
    LOVE ME, SHOVE MY DOG

6. **The Byrds:** (Also Garfield's favourite group of all time)
    HEY, MR. ICE-CREAM MAN

5. **Procol Harum:**
    A WHITER SHADE OF MAILMAN

4. **Abba:**
    GNAWING ME, GNAWING YOU

3. **Horst Jankowski:**
    A WALK IN THE BLACK FOREST GATEAU

2. **The Mamas and the Papas:**
    TUESDAY, TUESDAY

1. **Don McLean:**
    AMERICAN PIE

(Plus Odie's all-time hate – The Rolling Stones: GET YOUR KICKS ON ROUTE 66)

GARFIELD'S TOP TEN SUGGESTIONS FOR NEW OLYMPIC EVENTS

10. The dogput
9. Synchronised snoring
8. Long jump over pit of rabid wolves
7. Speedsnacking
6. Demolition bobsleds
5. Mice hockey
4. Fridge lift
3. Burpathon
2. Greco-Roman flea scratching
1. Eat till you explode!

"ODIE TRIED TO INVENT ONE OF THESE, BUT HE COULDN'T COUNT UP TO TEN!"

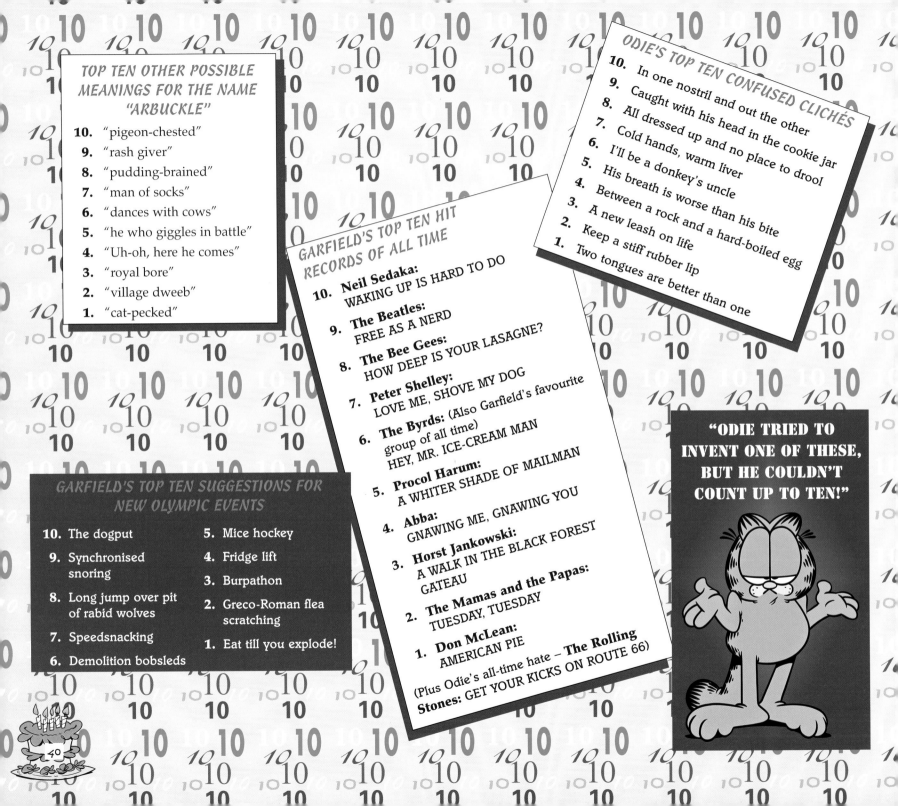

TOP TEN THINGS GARFIELD WOULD DO IF HE WON THE LOTTERY

10. Buy Jon a personality

9. Build a stall around his litter box

8. Hire some yobbos to rough up the neighbourhood

7. A refrigerator in every room!

6. Get a job, just so he could quit it

5. Send Odie to a clinic for problem droolers

4. Have his stomach enlarged

3. Get petted by a different babe every night

2. Pay some bills

1. Eat, sleep and look rich doing it

GARFIELD'S TOP TEN EXCUSES FOR NOT CATCHING MICE

10. "I thought it was a squeaky dustball."

9. "I tore a muscle in my paw."

8. "The mouse had a preservation order."

7. " I left my instincts in another life."

6. "Ghandi made me not do it."

5. "I come from a lazy home."

4. "Let other cats catch mice, I'll catch some 'Z's!"

3. "You mean mice aren't an endangered species?"

2. "I'm on a no-vermin diet."

1. "Would you stick a hairy, disease-carrying pest in **your** mouth?"

GARFIELD'S TOP TEN REASONS TO PARTY

10. Your place could use a good trashing.

9. A party demon has possessed your body.

8. You just like to make ice.

7. You simply can't think of anything boring to do.

6. Haven't annoyed your neighbours for a while.

5. Want to get some wear out of that lamp shade.

4. Your bio-rhythms are in "limbo" mode.

3. Good way to meet your local law enforcement officials.

2. Helps you to forget about the whole bummer "mortality" thing.

1. Because you can!

TOP TEN THINGS GARFIELD WOULD LIKE FOR HIS BIRTHDAY

10. Nermal deported

9. Pet goldfish, with a side order of fries

8. Combination back scratcher – spider whacker

7. Diving board for his food dish

6. Giant autographed poster of himself

5. Bird grater

4. Muzzle for Jon

3. Electric doggy prod

2. New cat bed with Italian restaurant attached

1. Party with 10,000 of his closest, gift-bearing friends

With special thanks to MARK ACEY, JIM KRAFT and SCOTT NICKEL

ART FOR GARFIELD'S SAKE

Over the years, Jim Davis and his art studio at PAWS in Indiana have produced an amazing variety of artwork. These Garfield pictures, in all their different styles, have been used to create the thousands of different Garfield licenced products we mentioned earlier.

In its own right, however, this art work is clever, funny and a delight to look at. So, as part of our celebration of all things Garfield, here are just some of the different Garfield poses – and our hero as you've probably never seen him before...

'DOODLE' STYLE

© PAWS

'PHOTOGRAPHIC' STYLE

© PAWS

42

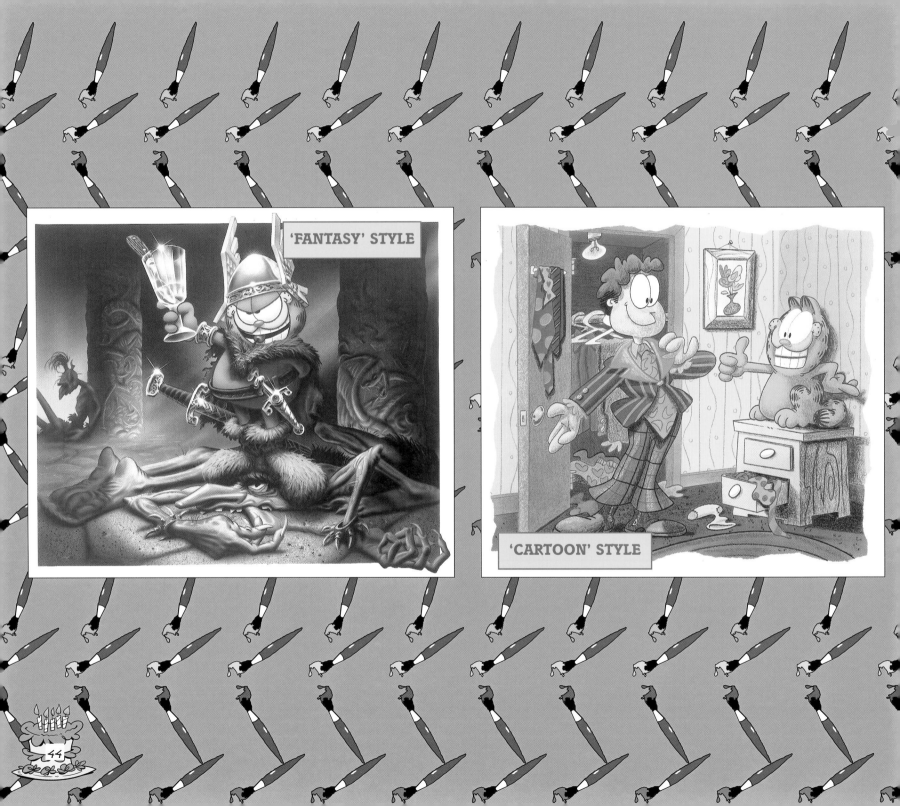

'FANTASY' STYLE

'CARTOON' STYLE

44

GARFIELD'S SUNDAY BEST

The Garfield Sunday strip is a completely different animal from the Garfield daily strip. (Er...better rephrase that...the two strips are very different, but they both feature the same greedy, sarcastic and loveable furry feline!) With up to eight pictures available instead of three, the Sunday strips allow room for more of a story, a bigger build-up to the final gag and more adventurous art work.

Better Shape Up!

In any newspaper, space is at a premium. And with Garfield appearing in over 2,600 different newspapers every Sunday, the strip has to be flexible in shape. So Jim Davis employs a cunning device – the extra picture. If you look closely at the strips in this section, you will see that the first picture next to the logo box and the second picture are very similar. You can drop the first one without losing the sense of the strip. So this means that the strip can be used in full, as it is here, giving it a wide extent, or the first picture can be ditched and the remaining pictures rearranged to produce a perfectly symmetrical tall shape. Ingenious, eh?

What's In The Box?

And what about those logo boxes at the beginning of each strip? Aren't they wonderful? They bear no relation to the story that follows, but they exhibit a breathtaking amount of wit, humour and artistic creativity.

The format was not always like this. The first Sunday strips had no title frame at all. (See page 10). Then a wide title was introduced that looked like this:

This box was used every Sunday right up until July 1985 when it was replaced by the new one-off logo. Since then, there has been a dazzling array of Garfield logo boxes which get funnier and more imaginative as the years go on.

So pretend it's Sunday morning and relax with the classic collection of GARFIELD® Sunday strips. We kick off with the one that featured the very first individual logo...

CAN'T THINK WHY I'M SMILING – I HAVE TO WORK THREE TIMES HARDER ON A SUNDAY!

45

KLACK!

JIM DAVIS 7-24

OKAY, HON, I'LL TAKE YOUR ORDER NOW

OH, AND HERE'S YOUR BALLOON

MY BALLOON?

© 1991 PAWS, INC.

WE'RE TRYING TO CREATE MORE OF A HAPPY FAMILY ATMOSPHERE

WE EVEN HAVE PONY RIDES OUT BACK

THAT SOUNDS LIKE FUN!

NOW, WHAT'LL YOU HAVE?

I'LL HAVE A HAMBURGER

JIM DAVIS 6-30

WELL, THERE GOES THE PONY RIDE

I'LL BE WAITING IN THE CAR

48

Garfield

PENCIL

CHANGE

COMB

CORN CHIPS

FORK

MUNCH MUNCH MUNCH

AH-HA!

THE REMOTE CONTROL

POP

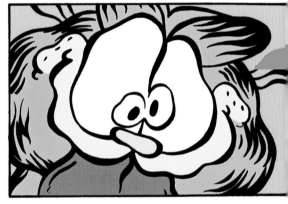
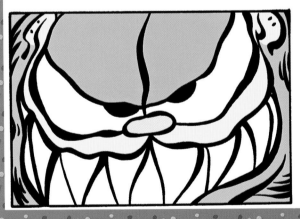

JIM DAViS 4-30

© 1995 PAWS, INC./Distributed by Universal Press Syndicate

THERE'S ORDINARY OLD COFFEE...

SLUP

YOWNG!

FLAP! FLAP! FLAP! FLAP!

WHIRRRRRRRR

AND THEN THERE'S "BOTTOM-OF-THE-POT-SITTING-PLUGGED-IN-ALL-DAY-COFFEE!"

© 1994 PAWS, INC./Distributed by Universal Press Syndicate

JIM DAVIS 8-7

55

A VERY GOOD YEAR

The main event of 1978 was, of course, the arrival of Garfield on June the 19th. But what else happened in that special year...and on the Big Day itself in years gone by? Here's all the Happy News from both great dates...

1978

That Sinking Feeling

In March, Oxford won the most famous Boat Race of recent times. They crossed the finishing line alone, their rivals Cambridge having sunk a mile from Putney Bridge.

Here Is The News

In February, Anna Ford became the first female newscaster on ITV. With her cool good looks and her educated, softly spoken voice, she was an immediate success. She has remained in broadcasting ever since and now works as a newscaster for the BBC.

Don't Cry For Me

The top musical of 1978 was 'Evita' by Andrew Lloyd-Webber and Tim Rice. The original West End production, starring David Essex and Elaine Page, was an immediate success and tickets sold out for several years ahead. Recently, of course, the musical was made into a very popular film starring Madonna.

Going...Going...Green

In January, Sweden became the first country in the world to ban aerosol sprays containing CFC gasses, which are harmful to the Ozone layer.

I GO EVEN GREENER WHEN JON CLEARS OLD LEFTOVERS OUT OF THE FRIDGE!

Keep it GREEN

Giant Step For Mankind

Also in February, the famous fossil hunter and archaeologist, Mary Leakey, announced that she had found footprints in Africa that were human in form and over 4 million years old.

Oh, Danny Boy!

1978 was very much John Travolta's year. Following his huge success in the 1977 film, 'Saturday Night Fever', he went on to play the part of Danny in the 1978 musical film, 'Grease'. Two of the songs from the film, 'You're The One That I Want' and 'Summer Nights', both duets with the film's co-star, Olivia Newton-John, went on to become Number One hits in the UK.

Float Like A Butterfly, Return Like A Bee

In February, boxing legend Mohammad Ali finally lost his world heavyweight boxing crown to Leon Spinks. But not for long! September saw a rematch in which Ali defeated Spinks, becoming the only man in history to have won the title three times.

TALKING OF SIMPLE, PRIMITIVE LIFE FORMS...

That Other Birthday

On July 26th, Louise Brown – the world's first "test-tube baby" – was born in Oldham General Hospital. Under the guidance of pioneering surgeon, Mr Patrick Steptoe, baby Louise was delivered by Caesarean section just before midnight and weighed in at just under 6 lbs. Amidst constant media attention, she has grown up to become a normal and healthy young lady who, like Garfield, celebrates her coming-of-age this year. Happy Birthday, Louise!

The First Of Many

In July, a young blond-haired cricketer called David Gower scored his first test century against New Zealand. One of the most fluent and elegant batsmen of all time, Gower went on to become captain of England. He is best known nowadays for his appearances in the hilarious TV sports quiz, 'They Think It's All Over'.

Strike Action

The world's first proper baseball game was played on this day in 1846. The game took place in New Jersey, USA, and followed official rules laid down by Alexander Cartwright, the "father" of American baseball. The match, between the New Yorks and the Knickerbockers, ended in victory to the New Yorks by 23 to 1.

Double First

King James VI of Scotland, son of Mary Queen Of Scots and Lord Darnley, was born in Edinburgh Castle on June 19, 1566. He took the throne at the tender age of one year old and, when old enough to rule for himself, proved a popular monarch. In 1603, following the death of Queen Elizabeth 1, James also became King Of England, the first person ever to rule both sides of the border. As James 1 of England, he proved far less popular than in his native land and his constant disputes with Parliament eventually led to the English Civil War.

Bobbies On Bicycles Two By Two

Today in 1829, Sir Robert Peel founded the Metropolitan Police in London. His aim in creating a recognised body of uniformed policemen was to cut down on crime and also help the poor. Laws at the time were exceedingly strict and even minor offences were punished by deportation or death. So by putting more policemen on the streets and preventing crime, less people suffered from the cruelty of the law.

I MUCH PREFER 'FLOWERS IN MY MOUTH!'

The Hippie Hippie Shakes

On Garfield's birthday in 1967, thousands of young people 'with flowers in their hair' were flocking to the Monterey Pop Festival. Organised by John Phillips and starring (amongst other big names) his own group, 'The Mamas And The Papas', the event was the climax of the famous "Summer Of Love".

So you think you know all about Garfield?

A Queen-Sized Quiz

It's time to get interactive! Here's an extended quiz about you-know-who which gets harder and harder as it goes along. So you'll need to be quite a Garfield anorak to get right to the end! Good luck!

1. Which day of the week does Garfield hate?

2. What is Jon's surname?

3. Who is Garfield's girlfriend?

4. Name Garfield's teddy bear?

5. Where do Jon's parents live?

6. What is Garfield's favourite food?

7. What is the name of the elderly couple who live next door to Jon?
   a) Madge and Harold
   b) Hubert and Reba
   c) Tony and Cherie

I'M OFF TO GET INTERACTIVE WITH MY SUPPER!

© PAWS

59

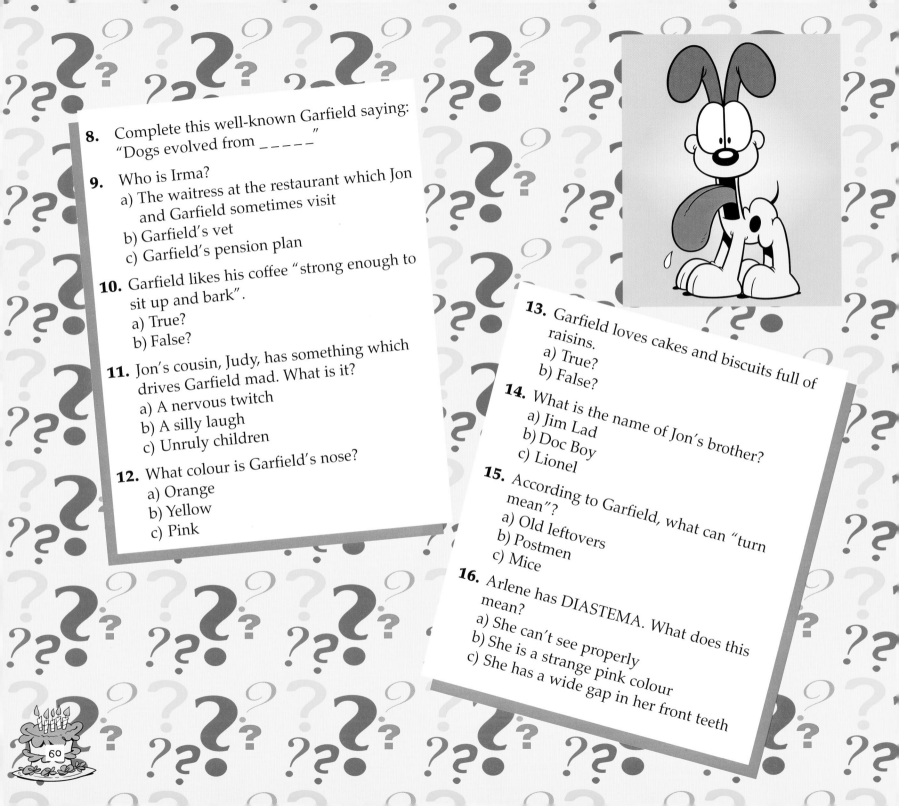

8. Complete this well-known Garfield saying: "Dogs evolved from _ _ _ _ _"

9. Who is Irma?
   a) The waitress at the restaurant which Jon and Garfield sometimes visit
   b) Garfield's vet
   c) Garfield's pension plan

10. Garfield likes his coffee "strong enough to sit up and bark".
    a) True?
    b) False?

11. Jon's cousin, Judy, has something which drives Garfield mad. What is it?
    a) A nervous twitch
    b) A silly laugh
    c) Unruly children

12. What colour is Garfield's nose?
    a) Orange
    b) Yellow
    c) Pink

13. Garfield loves cakes and biscuits full of raisins.
    a) True?
    b) False?

14. What is the name of Jon's brother?
    a) Jim Lad
    b) Doc Boy
    c) Lionel

15. According to Garfield, what can "turn mean"?
    a) Old leftovers
    b) Postmen
    c) Mice

16. Arlene has DIASTEMA. What does this mean?
    a) She can't see properly
    b) She is a strange pink colour
    c) She has a wide gap in her front teeth

17. In 1986, a two-week sequence of strips saw Garfield and all his friends (not to mention passers-by!) caught up in something. What was it?
a) A roller blind
b) Jon's Braces
c) 'Geeks Have Rights' protest movement

18. Who is Uncle Roy?
a) Jon's Uncle
b) A TV presenter who Garfield watches
c) Garfield's mother's new boyfriend

19. Which one of these is NOT a character Garfield has pretended to be?
AMOEBA MAN,
THE CAPED AVENGER,
KARATE CAT, ROLLERCLAW,
TIGER SHARK, SUMO CAT

20. Once (and only once), Jon managed a successful goodnight kiss with Liz the vet. What was Garfield's comment?
a) "Yuk!"
b) "Suck face, share germs"
c) "Human love...it's so glandular"

21. Once, Garfield tried to post Nermal to Timbucktu.
a) True?
b) False?

22. Can you fill in the two missing words in this sentence?
'In the longest sequence of strips ever published, Garfield ran away and joined the _ _ _ _ _ _ where he met _ _ _ _ _ the Clown.'

23. Who or what was Stretch?
a) Special trousers made to fit Garfield
b) A limo Jon hired for a date
c) Garfield's rubber chicken

24. Garfield has a cat friend called Ed who has lived his whole life in a certain place. Where?
a) Up a tree with squirrels
b) In a dustbin with mice
c) Down a hole with rabbits

25. Which one of these is NOT one of Garfield's favourite form of exercise?
DOUGHNUT DUNKING,
CHANNEL SURFING,   MICE CHASING,
A BRISK NAP,   DOG KICKING,
SPIDER SPLATTERING

61

26. Jon's mother is a terrible cook.
   a) True?
   b) False?

27. What fate befell Jon's pet frog, Herbie?

28. What is Odie called when he plays the drums on the fence with Garfield?

29. Garfield's favourite food, lasagne, was invented to give soldiers easy-to-carry, nourishing food. By which army?
   a) The Greeks
   b) The Romans
   c) The Egyptians

30. In which year did Garfield become the first comic strip in history to appear in over 2,500 newspapers around the world?
   a) 1993
   b) 1994
   c) 1995

FRIENDS, ROMANS, COUNTRYMEN, GIVE ME A CLUE!

62

At one time or another, most of us have had a Garfield poster up on our walls. They're bright, colourful and funny – just what you need to cheer you up on a cold, wet Monday morning.

To celebrate the art and humour of the Garfield poster, here's a small selection of the most popular. And we kick off with a very famous one which began life as the third panel of a 1985 daily strip and went on to become a best-seller...

ALL MY PERSONALITIES SAY "HI"

CATS ARE POETRY IN MOTION.

BEE-BU BEE-BU
BEE-BU BEE-BU
BEE-BU BEE-BU
BEE-BU BEE-BU
BEE-BU BEE-BU
BEE-BU BEE-BU
BEE-BU
BEE-BU
BEE-BU
BEE-BU
BEE-BU
BEE-BU
BEE-BU
BEE-BU

© PAWS

DOGS ARE GIBBERISH IN NEUTRAL.

ASSUME THE ATTITUDE

65

In A Perfect World...

Everything would be remote control

© PAWS

GARFIELD AND THE MILLENNIUM BUG

"Do I look silly in this, Garfield?" asked Jon.

"No," replied Garfield, shaking his head. "You look a complete and utter IDIOT!"

"Glad you like it, Garfield" continued Jon. "I'm going to wear it to Liz's Fancy Dress Party on New Year's Eve. I might even get a kiss like I did at 11:43 pm on December 19th 1981."

"And Odie might be a finalist in 'University Challenge'!" commented Garfield.

Jon was wearing a shabby Safari jacket he had bought in the Seventies, baggy brown shorts, long socks, open-toed sandals and a plastic bowl on his head, representing a pith helmet.

"I'm a fearless bug-hunter," he announced, "scouring the African Rain Forest for strange and exotic insects!"

"You're a nerd," said Garfield.

"And you," added Jon, plonking a big pair of plastic wings on Garfield and a cone on his nose, "are a giant killer wasp I keep catching in my net. All you have to do is buzz."

"Correction," murmured Garfield, hurrying away. "All I have to do is buzz OFF!"

Jon tried to grab Garfield, but only succeeded in catching his cardboard nose. TWANG! The cone sprang back on its elastic, hitting Garfield in the face.

"You've stung yourself, Garfield!" laughed Jon.

Then he noticed the ferocious glare on his cat's face and the claws gleaming in the bright kitchen light.

"The nose needs work!" said Jon, hastily.

Fortunately, moments later, Jon's personal computer began making a loud whistling noise. He hurried into the sitting room to fix it.

67

"Someone's trying to send an E-mail, but they can't get through," he cried.

"Maybe you shouldn't have changed your address to 'arbuc. deeply sad. com'," suggested Garfield.

"It's this wretched Millennium Bug!" exclaimed Jon, pressing the keyboard and gazing helplessly at the mass of squiggles on the screen. "I had the guy round to amend the software ahead of tomorrow night, but he's just messed everything up. Can you help, Garfield? Hey, Garfield, where are you...?" Jon looked up to see his pet outside, charging towards the terrified postman. Having torn the man's trousers to shreds, Garfield returned with a mouthful of ripped letters.

"Last raid of the Twentieth Century!" he said, proudly.

Garfield curled up on the sofa, leaving Jon taking his computer to pieces in a vain attempt to mend it. Despite his geeky master, Garfield was feeling at peace with the world. 1999 had been an excellent year. His 21st birthday had passed in a whirl of parties, presents and serious over-eating. Now New Year had almost arrived – the Twenty-First Century, a new Millennium... and the biggest party the world had ever known! There were bound to be mountains of food at Liz's house and Garfield imagined himself powering his way through it. But his dreams were shattered by the DING, DONG of the doorbell.

"Can you get that, Garfield?" called Jon. "I'm up to my elbows in disk-drive!"

Garfield slouched to the front door and opened it. On the step stood an elderly couple and a man who looked about Jon's age. They all wore dungarees and the younger man had a stalk of corn behind his ear.

"The Country and Western Convention's at the town hall down the road," said Garfield, knowing perfectly well who they were but still shutting the door in their faces. The bell rang again and, this time, Jon answered.

"Mom! Dad! Doc Boy!" exclaimed Jon. "What are you doing in town?"

"Well, slap mah hide an' cover me with hogswill!" proclaimed Garfield. "These good folks is come a-visitin' fer the big holiday!"

Garfield was right. Jon's family wanted to be together for the special New Year and had invited themselves to stay in town. They had written several times, but Garfield chewed the letters up. They had tried to phone, but Jon was always on the line trying to get a date. And they had stopped on their way up from the country to send "one of them new-fangled messages", but of course Jon's computer was down. So they turned up unexpectedly.

Scowling like a gargoyle, Garfield sat and watched suitcase after suitcase being brought in from the pick-up truck at the front of the house. His face soon brightened, however, when a tarpaulin was thrown back, revealing several tons of food.

"I wanna see my boys eatin' their way into the new Millennium," said Mrs Arbuckle.

Jon's brother expressed great interest in the dismantled computer.

"Gee willerkins!" exclaimed Doc Boy. "That pesky Millennium Bug can sure do a lot of damage!"

"No, that's not quite right..." began Jon.

"Reminds me of the time, 'bout '75 I think it was, we got a dose of Boll Weevil in our cotton. No sooner had we gotten rid of that critter than we got the Colorado Beetle in our spuds!"

Doc Boy went on and on with his farmyard reminiscences, so Jon gave up trying to explain.

Later that day, Jon took his folks on a sight-seeing tour around town. There was no more room in the car, so Garfield was left behind.

"I'm bored," sighed Garfield. "Bored, bored, bored!"

Then Garfield remembered his fancy dress outfit.

"Odie hasn't seen it yet," he chuckled. "So I could have some fun!"

Dressed up as the African killer bee, Garfield went in search of his faithful friend who was sleeping peacefully on the bed. Garfield lifted one of Odie's eyelids and made a fierce-looking face. Then he prodded him with a toasting fork which was acting as his 'sting'. Odie shot straight up in the air with a terrified yelp.

"Wow!" cried Garfield. "Houston – we have lift-off!"

Garfield was happily chasing the terrified Odie around the house when the door burst open and in came Doc Boy. He had forgotton his camera. But he took one look at Garfield and his eyes opened wide.

"There's the critter!" he cried.

The following day was New Year's Eve. Jon had promised to go round to Liz's house and help her prepare for the party.

"Haven't seen Garfield this morning," thought Jon, loading some glasses into his car. "But maybe it's just as well. He'd only be under my feet, scrounging for food."

Jon spent all day with Liz, although he did not really need to. He was trying to make her promise to give him a midnight kiss.

"Read my lips, Jon," sighed Liz, wearily.

"I am! I am!" cried Jon.

"I may or may not give you a kiss," said Liz, speaking deliberately slowly. "It all depends on how I feel at the time."

At six o'clock, Jon went home to change into his fancy dress outfit. He expected to find Garfield waiting for him, but there was still no sign of his pet.

"He'll come home when he's hungry," said Mrs Arbuckle, philosophically.

"Mom, he's ALWAYS hungry!" exclaimed Jon.

The evening wore on and Jon returned to Liz's, taking his family with him. (They did not need to dress up – their country clothes looked funny enough!) It was a good party and soon the Arbuckles were enjoying themselves. Jon, however, felt very miserable.

"Where's Garfield?" he wailed, almost in tears. "How can I party when he's gone missing?" Doc Boy noticed his brother's distress and came over to cheer Jon up.

"Hey, I caught that doggone Millennium Bug of yours," he said.

"What did it look like?" asked Jon, his eyes narrowing suspiciously.

"Big brute, he was," replied Doc Boy. "Orange and black...and fat as a prize-winning pumpkin."

"GARFIELD!" yelled Jon.

It turned out that Doc Boy had locked what he thought was a computer-wrecking insect in Jon's garden shed. With the minutes rapidly ticking away towards midnight, Jon raced home and rescued Garfield.

"It wasn't all bad," muttered Garfield, staggering out of the shed. "I managed to squish 416 spiders!"

Back at the party, Garfield made up for lost time and demolished all the food in the remaining five minutes before midnight. Then the clock struck twelve and, like billions of others around the globe, Liz and her guests welcomed the new century.

"And my kiss?" asked Jon.

"You may have it," agreed Liz, putting her arms round his neck. "I'm proud of the way you love that dreadful cat of yours."

Garfield looked away, making a disgusted face.

"Humans!" he muttered. "They never cease to bug me!"

WHO ARE YOU TRYING TO KID?

In a desperate attempt to relieve the boredom, Jon declared that Saturday night should be Quiz Night. He spent all week preparing a special set of questions which he gave to Garfield at 7pm. By 7.03, they were all done – and done correctly! So it was back to the nerdy games again!

Here's the quiz that Garfield tackled so effortlessly. It consists of a dozen amazing facts, nine of which are true and three of which are false. Can you match the clever fat cat and pick out the imposters?

Flat Cat

Mrs Lewis, from Ohio in the United States, owned a cat called Felix. One day, this unfortunate animal was run over and killed by a juggernaut lorry. Rather than being parted from her pet, Mrs Lewis took his flattened body to the local vet. Using a machine normally used to freeze-dry coffee, the vet freeze-dried Felix who returned home looking much the same as he did before, only a little flatter!

Dogs' Dinner

Lord Bridgewater, an English nobleman who lived in Paris at the end of the Eighteenth Century, was very rich and very eccentric. He used to give elaborate dinner parties – for dogs! These pampered pooches ate the very best food from the very best plates, dressed in miniature outfits that followed the latest fashions. They even wore special miniature shoes!

Make No Bones About It

Originally, bone china was exactly what its name implies – crockery made from bones. A German scientist, Gottfried von Reichspudding, discovered that powdered animal bones mixed with clay and then baked produced a beautifully clear and smooth clay from which they made plates and bowls. He sold his idea for a lifetime supply of beer and sausages to a business man in Dresden. Ever since, this city has been the capital of the German porcelain industry.

Shocking News

A stray dog wandered onto a railway line in Southern England one sunny afternoon. The resulting electric shock catapulted the creature right over a nearby hedge. A woman sitting in her garden watched him fly right over her head and land in the garden pond. She took the dog straight to the vet who examined him and found that he was none the worse for his ordeal!

A Spectre Calls

An American doctor named Weir Mitchell, who lived in Philadelphia during the last century, was awoken one night by a loud knocking on his door. He found a young girl standing on his doorstep, begging him to visit her sick mother. The doctor followed the girl to a rundown tenement building where he located and treated a woman who had once been a servant of his long ago. When he mentioned the brave little girl, the woman looked baffled. "My daughter died over a month ago," she said.
To prove it, she showed Mitchell the girl's shawl and shoes. They were exactly the same as the ones the girl had been wearing!

Back To The Grindstone

Historians believe that windmills did not exist in Europe before the Crusades. There is evidence that the returning Crusaders brought details of how windmills worked when they returned from the East. These machines were highly suited to the windy climate of Western Europe and appeared all over England, France, Germany and Holland after the Twelfth Century.

Blink And You Miss It

The cornea (the transparent lens of the eye) is the only part of the human body that is not nourished by oxygen in the blood. It derives its oxygen from the air outside.

Chew Chew Train

You may have heard how fallen leaves on the line have caused the delay of British trains, but this incident from Scotland is even more bizarre. A schoolgirl called Annie Oldiron threw her chewing gum out of the window. Unfortunately, the train was passing through a station at the time and the gum hit a guard, causing him to blow his whistle. This resulted in another train pulling out of the station before the passengers were ready. Fortunately, nobody was hurt – but several families were split up and many people left their luggage on the station platform.

Drink To Me Only With Thine Eyes

Frogs and toads use their eyes to help them eat! When swallowing, they close their eyelids and press down with their eyeballs, lowering the roof of their mouths against their tongues and so squeezing their food down into their mouths.

That Just About Raps It Up

Despite its recent success, rap music is not a new idea. Manuscripts have been found showing that the Aztecs of Ancient Mexico wrote and performed the same sort of fast-moving spoken poetry accompanied by music.

That'll Put Lead In Your Pencil

The Romans used ground-up lead as a sweetening agent and as a cure for upset stomach. They also drank wine out of lead goblets. Little did they realise how much they were poisoning themselves!

Tyred Out

Charles Goodyear – whose name is now synonymous with car tyres, especially those for racing cars – discovered how to process rubber by accident. One day, he spilt a mixture of rubber and sulphur on his stove and found that the resulting mixture was tough and flexible in all conditions. He called his discovery "vulcanised rubber". Unfortunately, he did not patent his idea properly and it was adapted by other people. As a result, Goodyear died a poor man and left huge business debts.

(Items 3, 8 and 10 are false)

73

THE WIT AND WISDOM OF GARFIELD

What do Plato, Aristotle, Descartes, Kant and Hegel have in common? They're all philosophers who most people have never heard of and, those that claim to, have never really read. The other thing these old guys have in common is that their combined philosophies pale into insignificance in comparison with the thoughts and sayings of Garfield!

All the important areas of life – eating, sleeping, insulting dogs and kittens – are covered by the fat cat's philosophy. Here's a little sample...

If you want to look thinner, hang around people fatter than you.

THE WORD" DIGNITY" IS NOT IN A DOG'S VOCABULARY

MOST DIETS ARE BEGUN TOMORROW.

When the going gets tough, I go to the fridge.

A BUSINESS IS ONLY AS STRONG AS ITS COFFEE.

ONE GOOD MEAL DESERVES ANOTHER

I'M NOT OVERWEIGHT. I'M UNDERTALL

"I LOVE IT WHEN I GET PHILOSOPHICAL"

SO MANY MEALS, SO LITTLE TIME

I'LL RISE...........BUT I WON'T SHINE.

EVERYONE HAS A RIGHT
TO MY OPINION.

LASAGNE...NATURE'S PERFECT FOOD

Never trust a smiling cat.

If it doesn't move, I'll eat it.

You're not born lazy —
it's an acquired skill

I'D RATHER BE HAPPY THAN THIN

THE EARLY CAT GETS THE SNACK

If you don't
indulge yourself,
nobody will.

75

EVERYTHING TASTES GOOD ON A DIET

FEBRUARY IS THE ARMPIT OF MONTHS.

SLOTH IS THE MOTHER OF INVENTION.

I'm a creature of habit...all the bad ones!

TOO MUCH FOOD IS NEVER ENOUGH

It's hard to be serious when you're naked.

Eat and sleep... there must be more to life than that — but I hope not!

LIFE IS SHORT. EAT NOW

TO EAT IS HUMAN, TO PIG OUT DIVINE

It's impossible to give a hug without getting one back.

HAVE YOU HUGGED YOUR TEDDY TODAY?

Pooky's Family Tree

Garfield's beloved teddy bear is the very latest in a long line of famous fictional teddies. In turn, these loveable little creatures are descendants of real teddy bears who, believe it or not, had not been invented a hundred years ago.

We decided to research Pooky's ancestry and delve deep into the fascinating history of the teddy bear...

In 1901, Theodore Roosevelt became President of the United States following the assassination of William McKinley. President Roosevelt – known to most people as Teddy Roosevelt – was a keen hunter and, in 1902, he attended a Grizzly bear hunt in the state of Mississippi. No bears were sighted for several days and, in a desperate attempt to please their important guest, the organisers of the hunt imported a captive bear cub. To his credit, Roosevelt refused to shoot this defenceless creature and the incident prompted a cartoon that appeared in the "Washington Star" newspaper on November 18th. It showed the President turning his back on a cute-looking little bear and bore the caption "Drawing The Line In Mississippi."

The cartoon was seen by Morris Michtom who, along with his wife, ran a small toy-making factory and shop in New York. Mrs Michtom made three soft toy bear cubs like the one in the cartoon and her husband sent one to the President, asking if he would object to the toy being called a "Teddy Bear" after the hunting incident. Roosevelt replied, saying he did not mind the name being used, but he did not think it would stimulate much business. How wrong he was! The first Teddy Bears with jointed arms and legs went on sale in America in 1903 and were an instant success. The Michtom's modest factory struggled to keep up with demand and, by 1907, they had expanded to become The Ideal Toy Corporation, one of the country's leading toy manufacturers.

Meanwhile, across the Atlantic, a similar phenomenon took place quite independently in Germany. At the Leipzig Trade Fair of 1903, a small family firm called **Steiff** exhibited a new jointed soft toy bear. Designed by Richard Steiff, who had seen some performing bears at a circus, it had been made by his aunt Margaret Steiff, a wheelchair-bound polio victim who had sewn soft toys all her life. These Steiff bears proved just as successful as their American rivals and, by 1907, the Steiff company were making a staggering 900,000 bears a year. These were exported all over Europe and the

first Teddy Bears to reach Britain came from Germany.

The craze for Teddy Bears reached its peak before the First World War. By 1920 they had become an established part of childhood and most countries had their own toy bear manufacturers. The best known British firm was **Farnells** who produced top quality plush teddies sold in big toy shops and at Harrods. One of these Farnell Teddy Bears was bought for a little boy called Christopher Robin by his father, A. A. Milne. The bear was called Edward, but he went on to become the world's most famous Teddy Bear under a different name, Winnie-the-Pooh.

"The Bear of Very Little Brain" first appeared in a poem published in "Punch" magazine in 1924. A. A. Milne then wrote two books, *Winnie-The-Pooh* (1926) and *The House at Pooh Corner* (1928) which established Pooh as one of the best-loved and most widely read childrens' characters since Alice in Wonderland. Pooh, Piglet, Kanga, Roo and Eeyore went on to delight an even wider audience when Walt Disney adapted their adventures into a classic cartoon film in 1966.

Three other fictional bears have rivalled Winnie-The-Pooh in terms of mass appeal. Rupert, invented by Mary Tourtel and continued by Alfred Bestall, has been a cartoon character in the "Daily Express" since November 1920, inspiring countless annuals, books and even a hit song ('We All Stand Together') by life-long admirer, Paul McCartney. Paddington Bear, in his famous floppy hat, duffle coat and Wellington boots, was invented by Michael Bond in 1956. Dispatched from darkest Peru and found on Paddington Station by the Brown family, this accident-prone little bear has amused generations of young children, both in books and on TV. Television has always been the home of Sooty, another mayhem-causing Teddy devised in the 1950s by Harry Corbett. Nowadays, Sooty, Sweep and Sue are managed (with the same degree of difficulty) by Harry Corbett's son, Mathew.

So we arrive at Pooky, the latest of the teddy bear superstars. Given that the Garfield® strip is published in over 2,500 different newspapers every day, Pooky is known and loved by hundreds of millions of people all around the world! Now you'd think that Garfield would be jealous, having to share his precious little buddy with so many others. Not a bit of it! Garfield knows the truth:

"Pooky is a one-cat teddy bear!"

© PAWS

I love my teddy bear

The Birthday Boy

Garfield is like the Queen in more ways than one. Not only, as he frequently claims, is he "Queen-sized", he also has two birthdays – a real one and an official one.

Garfield's real birthday occurred on an unknown date before the strip began in the kitchen of Mamma Leoni's Italian restaurant. Some serious imprinting took place, explaining Garfield's lifelong passion for lasagne, pizza and all things pasta. By consuming huge quantities of Italian food from day one, our hero's kittenhood was over in the twinkling of an eye and he very quickly became the giant cat we all know and love. By the time we see him with Jon, he is a fully grown cat.

Garfield's official birthday – the one we are celebrating here – is the anniversary of his first appearance in those 41 newspapers on June 19th, 1978. Every year since this famous debut, Jim Davis has devoted a whole week of strips to Garfield's birthday celebrations, culminating in the Big Day itself. So we have culled the latter, stretching from his first birthday in 1979 to his twentieth in 1998, and put them together in a montage so we can enjoy some real "happy returns of the day"...

1979

1980

1981

1982

HAPPY BIRTHDAY, GARFIELD!

JIM DAVIS

GULP!

© 1982 PAWS, INC.

MAYBE YOU SHOULD HAVE BLOWN THE CANDLES OUT FIRST

6-19

1983

GARFIELD®

THIS IS THE PERFECT SURPRISE. IT'S MUCH TOO EARLY FOR GARFIELD TO BE UP

JIM DAVIS

6-19

SSSH

HE'S A YEAR OLDER TODAY, YOU KNOW

SURPRISE!

© 1983 PAWS, INC.

AND A YEAR SNEAKIER

83

1984

1985

1986

1987

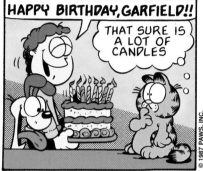

1988

HAPPY BIRTHDAY, GARFIELD! READY FOR YOUR CAKE?

JUST A MINUTE!

OKAY!

BRING THAT SUCKER ON!

© 1992 PAWS, INC

JIM DAVIS 6-19

HAPPY BIRTHDAY, GARFIELD!

AH, YES. 'TIS TRUE I HAVE TRAVERSED FIFTEEN NOTABLE YEARS WITHIN THIS MORTAL COIL. THIS AUSPICIOUS OCCASION CALLS FOR AN APPROPRIATE ACKNOWLEDGMENT

FEED ME!

6-19 JIM DAVIS

© 1993 PAWS, INC

Here's Garfield during his angst-filled teenage years. He worried a lot about spots – should he kick Odie on the same spot or vary it from day to day? He also fretted a great deal about the environment – surely Jon should buy a bigger house to keep his collection of postmens' trousers and spat-out raisins!

© PAWS

1996

1997

1998

STARTING FROM SCRATCH

The Lowdown On FLEAS

"Mark but this flea" wrote John Donne, the 17th Century English poet. Donne was a great admirer of fleas – he felt they helped to unite him with his coy mistress by biting them both!

Garfield is not so keen. As far as he's concerned, fleas are like Mondays, Odie and food commercials when he's on a diet – a terrible irritation!

So who's right? Decide for yourself as you digest these info-bytes about these fascinating little mites. (You must be itching to find out more about them!)

There are about 1,600 different types of flea around the world.

All fleas are parasites. They cannot live on their own; they have to live on another animal.

Fleas have specially adapted mouths that enable them to bite and suck the blood of their hosts. (This explains their scientific name Siphonaptera, which means "blood-sucking insect".)

Usually, fleas feed every day, but they are very hardy and can survive for several months without any food.

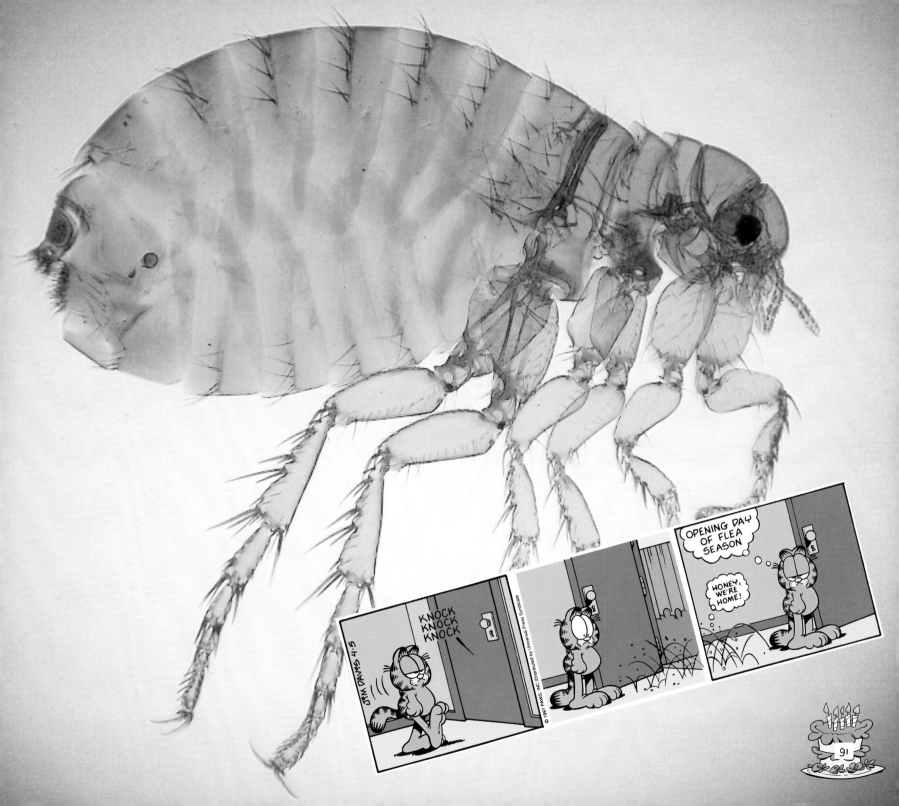

Cat fleas, dog fleas and human fleas are all separate species and have differently shaped heads, but they don't stick exclusively to their main hosts. Cat fleas also infest dogs and man; dog fleas can live on a wide variety of mammals including pigs!

Cat fleas reproduce at a phenomenal rate. An adult female sheds up to 20 eggs a day and produces about 500 eggs in a normal lifetime.

Fleas have a special leathery skin that protects them from injury when their hosts scratch themselves.

Human fleas are very long-lived. In suitable conditions, an individual flea can survive for anything up to 18 months.

The most amazing thing about all fleas is their ability to jump. Given their tiny size, the height they can reach and the distance they can travel is truly astonishing. It has been estimated that, if a man had an equal jumping ability, he would travel approximately five city blocks!

Dog fleas have an unusual male/female size difference. The female can grow to 4mm long, but the male only reaches about 2mm.

Some fleas are very fussy about whom they live with. The shrew flea, for example, will only live on shrews and other types of rodent!

HAPPINESS IS A WARM FLEA COLLAR

Most fleas are irritating and unpleasant pests, but rat fleas have a more sinister side. In the past, they have been responsible for transmitting bubonic plague. The Black Death of the Middle Ages and the Great Plague of the 1660s were caused by the bite of infected rat fleas.

92

Adapted from material previously published in the Garfield Annual

INFANCY

This first stage of your life has a great deal to recommend it. Think about it —

* You're expected to sleep nearly all of the time
* You can demand food whenever you like
* Loud burps are greeted with cries of delight
* Absolutely everything is done for you

Get through the stage of crawling on all fours as quickly as you can and start walking on two legs. I have passed through this phase myself and I much prefer being upright. You'll find escaping with stolen food and kicking the dog is infinitely easier.

Try to be original when you say your first words. Avoid old-hat phrases like "Mama" and "Dada" - instead, plump for something important and meaningful like:

"Pizza!"

"With chips, please"

or

"If you don't stop saying "coochey-coo", I'm gonna ram my dummy up your nose!"

Perfect your timing so that you cry whenever your grown-up is asleep, throw-up on his shoulder when his jacket's just been cleaned and ensure your nappy needs changing again immediately after it's been changed.

When in your pram, throw out your toys in all directions with the force of cruise missiles. Your grown-up will think you're looking for the reassurance of having them returned, but in fact you are attempting to brain any passing birds or animals.

Break into a big, beaming smile whenever anyone looks at you. Then you can get away with MURDER!

COOL CAT

CHILDHOOD

Never lose your sense of wonder. Keep saying things like:

"I wonder what's for dinner?"

"I wonder what I'm getting for my birthday?"

"I wonder what will happen if I run over the dog with my remote-control Bigfoot?"

Don't be a child statistic and sit in front of the TV for an average of three hours a day. Make it six...or eight!

Learning to read and write is vitally important. When your grown-ups spell out messages to one another, thinking you won't understand, you'll know exactly what they're saying and discover what you're getting for your birthday and where it's hidden.

Whatever you do, don't play run-of-the-mill, traditional childish games like skipping, hopscotch and conkers. Instead, invent your own state-of-the-art pastimes for the new Millennium. I recommend:

* Bird badminton (No need to buy shuttlecocks)
* Pass-the-parcelled-up-kitten
* Tongue tug-o-war (With your dog)

and

* Can I sit on your lap and claw you to pieces? (With your human)

Maintain the established junior outlook towards the opposite sex. Treat your boyfriend or girlfriend as an absolute equal in all things, but indicate your love for him or her by hitting them repeatedly with your lunchbox and then running away.

Make sure all your new toys are taken to pieces or smashed by 12 noon on Christmas Day.

From about the age of eight, dress, talk and behave like a teenager. (See next Section). At the same time, retain your passion for pre-school TV shows and have so many teddies on your bed that you can't get in it.

94

ADOLESCENCE

This stage of your life is not a lot different from the first and has the same sort of things to recommend it –

* You're expected to sleep nearly all the time

* You can demand food (and clean shirts) any time of the day or night

* Loud burps are now an expression of your adulthood

* Absolutely everything is done for you (except channel surfing)

Don't be ashamed of your spots. On the contrary, be proud of them. They proclaim to the world that you have a high-calorie diet of sugar, fatty food and pasta.

Beware of crushes – they can be very upsetting. I can remember having a pineapple crush with an ice-cream float that upset my stomach for weeks.

Don't be too forward on your first date. When you're standing on his or her doorstep, saying goodnight, don't come out with some pushy phrase like:

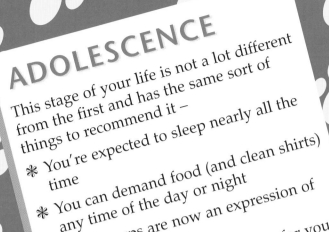

"May I kiss you?"

Go for something conservative and restrained, like:

"Wanna lip wrestle?"

Don't learn to drive. It is expensive, nerve-wracking and puts you in a position of totally unwanted independence.

Do buy an old car with a view to restoring it, but only get as far as taking it all to pieces and leaving it blocking the drive.

This is the time of your life when you are expected to travel, explore and widen your horizons. So make sure you watch DISCOVERY or NATIONAL GEOGRAPHIC channels and only hire out adventure games for your computer.

Don't, under any circumstances, be taken in by the work ethic. Remember what that English guy said:

"Work is the curse of the coffee-drinking class."

So chill out and drop out. Eat, sleep and abuse your betters. In other words – act like a cat!

GARFIELD GRAFFITI

SHOPPING

MONEY ISN'T EVERYTHING. THERE'S also plastic

LIFE'S a mall

THESE are my formative shopping years

NO problem is too big to shop away

WHEN I shop, I shop BIG

TO shop or NOT to shop? That's a stupid question!

Everyone has a place, MINE is at the mall

I love curling up with a good catalogue

alarm clocks were made to be broken

Buddy, can you spare some sleep?

SLEEP – don't leave bed without it
available in beds everywhere
it will make your night
recommended by 10 out of 10 doctors
recommended by 10 out of 10 cats

the only good morning
is a late morning

...AND DREAMS

You know you're
dreaming when – diets are outlawed
they ask you to model swimsuits
watching exercise makes you lose weight
elves do all your housework

PARTIES

study short, party long

WELCOME to party central

Party 'til the cows come home.
then party with the cows

those are my peak party years

serious times call for serious partying

WE must boldly par[ty]
where no one has partied before

Party 'til the cows call the cops

I'm considering a career in partying

the best parties have to be hosed out

Party alert! Party alert! this is not a drill!

GARFIELD'S SECRET BIRTHDAY DIARY

At last! The secret is out! Over the past 21 years, Garfield has been keeping a personal diary. And he has given us special access to it for the purpose of this book.

Here are some extracts from his birthday on June 19th over the years...

1982

As a treat for my fourth birthday, Jon took me to see the hit musical, 'Cats'. He loved it, but I was most unimpressed. Okay, those guys could sing and dance a bit, but that's all. Could they breathe under food? Could they sleep through an earthquake? Could they kick the dog, chase the postman and squash six spiders all at the same time? You bet your sweet life they couldn't! (Anyway, what are humans doing, pretending to be cats? We're two different species. The idea of a human behaving like a cat or – worse still – a cat behaving like a human is TOTALLY ridiculous!)

1984

This year, for my sixth birthday, I was taken to see a film about some guy called Mozart. Gee, what a geek! Some of his antics make Jon look like one of the Pilgrim Fathers. I grant you he wrote a few decent tunes, but they don't hold a candle to the jingle on the pepperoni pizza commercial on TV.
Now THAT'S music!

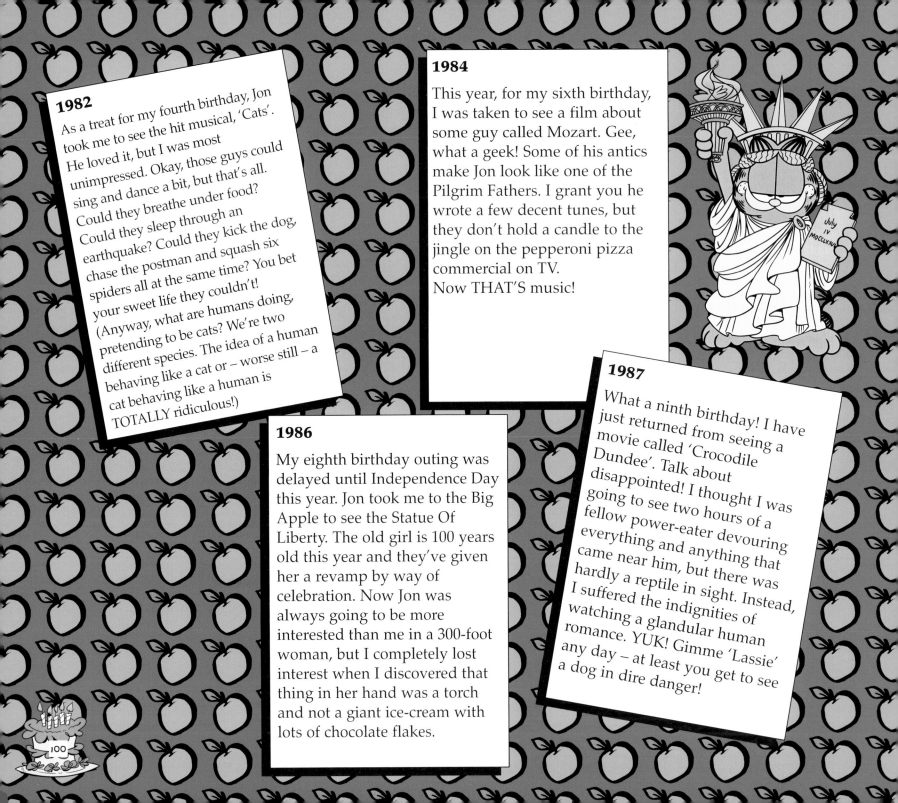

1986

My eighth birthday outing was delayed until Independence Day this year. Jon took me to the Big Apple to see the Statue Of Liberty. The old girl is 100 years old this year and they've given her a revamp by way of celebration. Now Jon was always going to be more interested than me in a 300-foot woman, but I completely lost interest when I discovered that thing in her hand was a torch and not a giant ice-cream with lots of chocolate flakes.

1987

What a ninth birthday! I have just returned from seeing a movie called 'Crocodile Dundee'. Talk about disappointed! I thought I was going to see two hours of a fellow power-eater devouring everything and anything that came near him, but there was hardly a reptile in sight. Instead, I suffered the indignities of watching a glandular human romance. YUK! Gimme 'Lassie' any day – at least you get to see a dog in dire danger!

1988

Guess what happened today, dear diary? My tenth birthday party was interrupted by a door-to-door salesman, flogging computers. He insisted they were the thing of the future and said we must have one if we want to travel down the new information superhighway. I didn't look too keen. After all, it would need to have plenty of lamp posts for Odie and Pizza Stops every couple of miles.

1991

Unlucky 13? Not a bit of it! I had a really cool birthday this year...all thanks to Odie. It's the early Nineties now and it's really fashionable to be a YUPPIE – a young, upwardly mobile person. So, as part of my birthday bash, I gave Odie the biggest kick of all time and sent him shooting straight upwards. HA, HA! Odie, the yuppie puppy!

June 19, 1993

Queued for four hours to see 'Jurassic Park'. Couldn't get in. Went to Burger Bar instead.

June 20, 1993

Insisted on queuing again. Another four hours. Still couldn't get in. Went to Pizza Parlour.

June 21, 1993

Queued again. Same result. Went to Italian Restaurant and Ice-Cream Palace.

June 22, 1993

Fourth time, got rumbled. Jon spotted Odie letting everyone ahead in the queue. Finally got to see film. Very impressive. If ever I'm reincarnated, I'd like to come back as a cloned T-Rex.

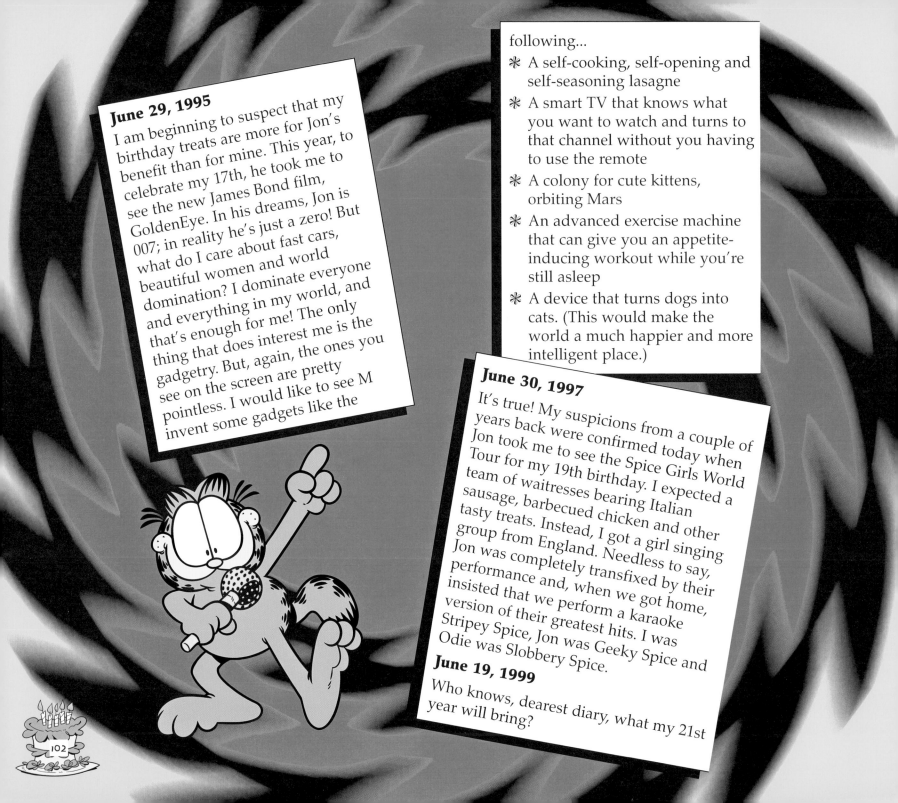

June 29, 1995

I am beginning to suspect that my birthday treats are more for Jon's benefit than for mine. This year, to celebrate my 17th, he took me to see the new James Bond film, GoldenEye. In his dreams, Jon is 007; in reality he's just a zero! But what do I care about fast cars, beautiful women and world domination? I dominate everyone and everything in my world, and that's enough for me! The only thing that does interest me is the gadgetry. But, again, the ones you see on the screen are pretty pointless. I would like to see M invent some gadgets like the

following...

* A self-cooking, self-opening and self-seasoning lasagne
* A smart TV that knows what you want to watch and turns to that channel without you having to use the remote
* A colony for cute kittens, orbiting Mars
* An advanced exercise machine that can give you an appetite-inducing workout while you're still asleep
* A device that turns dogs into cats. (This would make the world a much happier and more intelligent place.)

June 30, 1997

It's true! My suspicions from a couple of years back were confirmed today when Jon took me to see the Spice Girls World Tour for my 19th birthday. I expected a team of waitresses bearing Italian sausage, barbecued chicken and other tasty treats. Instead, I got a girl singing group from England. Needless to say, Jon was completely transfixed by their performance and, when we got home, insisted that we perform a karaoke version of their greatest hits. I was Stripey Spice, Jon was Geeky Spice and Odie was Slobbery Spice.

June 19, 1999

Who knows, dearest diary, what my 21st year will bring?

GARFIELD SOUND BYTES

Don't you just love cartoon sound effects? All those "ARRGHS" and "SHRIEKS" and "SPLATS". And when you see them in print, as you do in a Garfield strip, they're always set in coloured letters as high as a house. Wonderful stuff!

The next three pages are a celebration of Garfield sound effects – an hilarious audio-visual mixture that you need to say out loud to receive the full benefit. But make sure nobody is listening.

YAWN

PTOOEY

HUG

SLURP

Mice Are Rather Nice

Right from the start, Garfield has made it clear he refuses to catch mice. His attitude has always been:

"Show me a good mouser and I'll show you a cat with bad breath."

Much to Jon's annoyance, Garfield happily tolerates the intruders in his household and the two species live side by side in a state closely resembling symbiosis (that's a posh name for two different animals living in support of each other).

Maybe it's time we found out a bit more about Garfield's little furry friends...

Mice originated on the grassy plains of Asia. Over the centuries, they spread thoughout Europe and have been carried by man to the Americas and Australia. They are now found in differing forms all over the world.

Like rats and certain insects, mice are one of the most common animals on earth. They breed at a phenomenal rate. Most types of mice are capable of reproducing when only three months old and females can have up to twelve young in a litter and several litters a year. So the world's total mouse population is impossible to estimate.

Mice are rodents. That means they are gnawing animals with a single pair of chisel-like teeth at the front of their mouths and none at the back. They can eat almost anything. Cereals like wheat and barley are their favourite diet, but they also eat protein foods such as cheese, nuts and meat. They have been known to eat chalk, soap, plaster, paste and glue!

As well as destroying food crops, mice can be a pest by spreading diseases such as typhus and plague. However, they perform a useful (and often unrecognised) service to man by providing food for other larger animals such as owls and foxes who would otherwise take more valuable food.

The **house mouse** (Mus musculus) is the most common sort of mouse and the one most people have seen. It is remarkably adaptable and can survive in the blazing heat of the tropics or the freezing cold of Antarctica. Its name comes from its fondness for sharing human dwellings, but these mice are equally at home in storage buildings like warehouses, rice paddies, fields of corn and sugar cane, marshes and coal mines.

Most house mice have brown-grey fur which is slighty paler underneath, large eyes and ears, and a pointed nose. They are 7- 10 cm (3-4 ins) long with a thick, scaly tail of about the same length. Males and females look very similar and are hard to tell apart.

The house mouse has poor eyesight, but acute senses of hearing, smell and taste. Its long whiskers are extremely sensitive and are used to guide it through narrow spaces. It is also a remarkably good climber with an incredible sense of balance, enabling it to run up and down walls, fences, pipes or anything vertical with ease. House mice are good at jumping considering their size, and they can also swim.

107

The harvest mouse (Micromys minutus), sometimes known as the 'red mouse' or 'red ranny' because of its russet-brown colouring, is one of the smallest mammals in Europe. A fully grown adult only measures 6-7½ cm (3 ins) and weighs a mere 6-8 grams (less then ⅓ oz). Harvest mice live in fields of cereal crops (hence their name) and feed off the grain, supplementing their diet with insects, butterflies, moths and caterpillars.

Because they are small, light and agile, harvest mice can climb and swing on the stalks of wheat and corn like mini-acrobats. Their tails are very important in this. When climbing, they twist them around the stalk and act like an extra foot; when descending, they use their tails like a brake. They build their nests amongst the stalks, sometimes as high as 1 metre (3ft) above the ground. Their young are safer from predators there.

Harvest mice have many enemies. Weasels, stoats, foxes and even toads will attack them and they are the favourite food of the barn owl. Man, of course, disturbs their habitat, when the cereal crops are cut down in the autumn and stubble-burning is another great hazard. Cold and wetness, however, are the greatest dangers – harvest mice are just too small to cope with bad weather. Despite all this, they continue to thrive. If you are lucky, you can spot them going about their business amongst the waving corn.

There are many other interesting and unusual types of mice. The singing mouse is so called because it emits a faint twittering sound that sounds musical. The waltzing mouse has an inherited faulty sense of balance and cannot move in a straight line. The marsupial mouse has a pouch for its young like the kangaroo to which it is related, while the pocket mouse has little pouches outside its cheeks in which food can be stored. The white mouse, which many children keep as pets, is a specially bred variant of the house mouse.

DON'T GIMME THAT STUFF ABOUT MOUSERS – SHOW ME **ANY** CAT WHO DOESN'T HAVE BREATH THAT STRIPS PAINT

VARIATIONS ON A THEME

It is easy to forget, amidst the plethora of books, videos, soft toys and countless other merchandise, that Garfield is, first and foremost, a newspaper cartoon character. In fact, he is the best known newspaper cartoon character ever, appearing in more newspapers than anyone else since the genre began at the turn of this century.

Someone once said that the British football season is not so much a competition but more of a marathon. This may be true, but at least the football teams get a break in the summer and a fresh start in the Autumn. Not so the newspaper cartoonist. His job is a **permanent** marathon, a 365-day-a-year job from which there is no escape. And every single day the job has to be done well, otherwise the strip will not be funny. Some task! So how is it done?

The first answer is, of course, talent. Jim Davis and his team are the best in the business – gifted, highly creative and very professional. But there is a trick of the trade which they employ to great effect: the **running gag**. Jokes and themes reoccur throughout the strip, changing slightly all the

time. This turns the marathon nature of the job to the cartoonist's advantage. There is plenty of time to explore a joke to the full. And these running gags get funnier as they go along, adding layer upon layer to what has gone before. It is like a variation in music, a theme that returns again and again in a different form.

Looking closely at the Garfield Strip, we have identified 36 reoccurring themes. (In fact, there are more, but we don't have room for them all!) The section that follows highlights one example of all the themes. Let's hope we have chosen your favourite...

"ASK THE CARTOONIST GUY TO VARY THIS FOR A DEEP-PAN PEPPERONI PIZZA!"

GARFIELD

ALIVE AND KICKING

SOME LIKE IT HOT... AND STRONG

MR. ENTERTAINMENT

110

REVOLTING MOULTING

SCOURGE OF THE SPIDER

SOOOOOO LAZY!

A DATE, A DATE, MY KINGDOM FOR A DATE!

ALL GOOD PALS AND JOLLY GOOD COMPANY

THE GREAT OUTDOORS

THE BUSINESS OF EATING...

...AND SLEEPING

ENTER THE CUTE KITTEN

113

THE EVER-CHANGING SEASONS I

THE EVER-CHANGING SEASONS II

THOSE MYSTERIOUS SPLUTS

A FRIDGE TOO FAR

'TIS THE SEASON TO BE GREEDY

HAPPY HOGMANAY

ZWIP ZWIP ZWIP ZWIP ZWIP ZWIP

I HATE MONDAYS

DIS GUY'S IN DISGUISE

THE CAPED AVENGER! FASTER THAN A SPEEDING DELIVERY TRUCK! TOUGHER THAN TAFFY!

ABLE TO EAT A LARGE PEPPERONI PIZZA IN A SINGLE BITE!

...WITH ANCHOVIES!

BORED, BORED, BORED

SYNCHRONIZED BOREDOM

116

FRIENDS FOREVER

POOKY, YOU SURE KNOW HOW TO SPOIL A GOOD BAD MOOD!

BECAUSE THEY'RE THERE

BEING STUCK IN A TREE ISN'T SO BAD

I'LL JUST SIT HERE AND ENJOY THE VIEW

...FOR THE REST OF MY LIFE

DISCERNING VIEWER

WELCOME TO "QUANTUM PHYSICS AND YOU"

CLICK CLICK CLICK

WHOA! LOOK OUT!

WHEW! I ALMOST SAW SOMETHING WORTHWHILE

117

CHECK OUT THAT CUTE GIRL OVER THERE!

AND CHECK OUT HER BIG BOYFRIEND RETURNING WITH ICE CREAM!

ACTUALLY, IT'S KIND OF REFRESHING

DIET IS 'DIE' WITH A 'T'

I KNOW YOU'RE SICK OF CARROT STICKS, SO I FIXED YOU SOMETHING DIFFERENT

DICED CARROTS!

BOY! THAT'S UNCOMFORTABLE

IF ONLY THEY COULDN'T TALK

HI, FATTY

...FATTY-FATTY-FAT-FAT-FATSO. FAT-FAT-FATTY-FAT-FATSO-FAT FATSTER-FATTY-FAT-FAT...

FAT-FATTY-FAT-FAT... I'M COUNTING THE DAYS TILL HIS BATTERY DIES

118

DOG DAY AFTERNOONS

FIGHTING THE FLAB

FEATHERED FRIENDS

COUNTRY BOYS

I SAY, WAITRESS!

MORNINGS R NOT US

WELL, LOOK WHO FINALLY GOT UP

IS IT GARFIELD, OR MISTER GRUMPY?

WE DON'T LIKE MISTER GRUMPY

AND MISTER GRUMPY DOESN'T LIKE YOU

YOU SAY MAILMAN AND WE SAY POSTMAN

MAILMAN'S HERE

AIEEEEEEEE!

WHAT WAS THAT?

WELL NOW, POSSIBLY THERE COULD BE A LARGE, UNATTRACTIVE INSECT IN THE MAILBOX... MAYBE

DEEPLY PHILOSOPHICAL

GARFIELD, SOMETIMES I HAVE TO ASK THE BIG QUESTIONS

WHEN'S LUNCH?

LIKE, WHAT IS MY PURPOSE?

TO BUY DOUGHNUTS

WHY AM I HERE?

TO FEED THE CAT

121

AND NOW A FAREWELL NOTE FROM THE BIG GUY...

Okay, everyone, that's enough! As you say over there, all this praise, adoration and adulation is doing my head in!

Hope you've enjoyed my little birthday extravaganza. We must do it again soon. How about next week? We could celebrate Odie's Coming-Of-Mental-Age – he now has the I.Q. of a two-year-old.

Now don't you go worrying that I'm going to retire. I mean, you can't give up work if you never do any, can you? So keep looking out for me and, barring a world ink shortage, I'll be spreading my unique brand of humour and my stomach for another 21 years.

Thanks for coming to my party. All this celebrating has made me work up an appetite. Anyone seen that ten-ton lasagne?

PARTY ON!

The fun doesn't stop here! There's a whole host of other Garfield books available from Ravette Publishing. They're on sale in bookshops all over the country, or you can order them direct. Please contact:

RAVETTE PUBLISHING LIMITED
Unit 3, Tristar Centre, Star Road, Partridge Green,
West Sussex RH13 8RA
Tel: 01403 711443, Fax: 01403 711554, Email: ravettepub@aol.com

Here's the complete list...

Garfield Pocket Books

This long-running series is a true best-seller. To date, a staggering 6½ million copies have been sold...and they're still going strong.

These are the latest –

Garfield
Shove At First Sight
JIM DAVIS
ISBN: 1-85304-990-5
PRICE: £2.99

Garfield
To Eat Or Not To Eat?
(That is a silly question!)
JIM DAVIS
ISBN: 1-85304-991-3
PRICE: £2.99

Flying High
ISBN: 1 85304 043 6 £2.99

A Gift For You
ISBN: 1 85304 190 4 £2.99

Going Places
ISBN: 1 85304 242 0 £2.99

Great Impressions
ISBN: 1 85304 191 2 £2.99

The Gladiator
ISBN: 1 85304 941 7 £2.99

Hangs On
ISBN: 1 85304 784 8 £2.99

Happy Landings
ISBN: 1 85304 105 X £2.99

Here We Go Again
ISBN: 0 948456 10 8 £2.99

In The Pink
ISBN: 0 948456 67 1 £2.99

The Irresistible
ISBN: 1 85304 940 9 £2.99

In Training
ISBN: 1 85304 785 6 £2.99

Just Good Friends
ISBN: 0 948456 68 X £2.99

Le Magnifique!
ISBN: 1 85304 243 9 £2.99

Let's Party
ISBN: 1 85304 906 9 £2.99

On The Right Track
ISBN: 1 85304 907 7

On Top Of The World
ISBN: 1 85304 104 1 £2.99

Pick Of The Bunch
ISBN: 1 85304 258 7 £2.99

The Reluctant Romeo
ISBN: 1 85304 391 5 £2.99

Says It With Flowers
ISBN: 1 85304 316 8 £2.99

Strikes Again
ISBN: 0 906710 62 6 £2.99

Wave Rebel
ISBN: 1 85304 317 6 £2.99

With Love From Me To You
ISBN: 1 85304 392 3 £2.99

WHY NOT COLLECT THEM ALL?

And don't forget these...

Garfield Classic Collection

Each book is a bumper edition containing 366 all-time favourite strips.

ISBN: 1 85304 970 0
Price: £4.99

ISBN: 1 85304 971 9
Price: £4.99

THREE TIMES THE SIZE...THREE TIMES THE FUN!

126

Garfield Theme Books

These sumptuous 64-page books feature selected strips on a given theme, printed in full colour.

Available September

Garfield's Guide To **HEALTHY LIVING**

JIM DAVIS

ISBN: 1 85304 972 7   Price: £3.99

Garfield's Guide To **SUCCESSFUL LIVING**

JIM DAVIS

ISBN: 1 85304 973 5   Price: £3.99

Garfield's Guide to Behaving Badly
ISBN: 1 85304 892 5
£3.99

Garfield's Guide to Insults
ISBN: 1 85304 895 X
£3.99

Garfield's Guide to Pigging Out
ISBN: 1 85304 893 3
£3.99

Garfield's Guide to Romance
ISBN: 1 85304 894 1
£3.99

Garfield Address and Birthday Book Gift Set

The Garfield Address Book (containing 80 pages) offers ample space for recording the details of family and friends, whilst The Garfield Birthday Book (containing 64 pages) offers an extensive birth or anniversary planner, special birthday pictures, strips, ideas for party food and drink and a fascinating famous birthdays list.

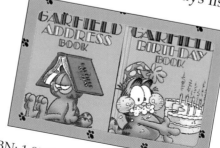

ISBN: 1 85304 918 2   Price: £7.99 (inc VAT)

MAKES AN IDEAL PRESSIE!

127

And finally, the companion publication to this book...

Garfield 21st Birthday Party Sticker Book

Designed for Garfield's younger fans or those still young at heart (remember Garfield's motto:)

"You're only young once, but you can be immature forever!"

This superb Sticker Book is packed with puzzles and activities, not to mention the strip pages, the brand new story and the pull-out-poster and the double page of colourful stickers you use to complete the book.

ON SALE NOW

GREAT VALUE AT ONLY £2.50

This is what he looks like today!